Breaking
THE CYCLE

By:

Tosha Cook

CONTENTS

Chapter 1

Wendy and I rode up to the Techwood housing projects where she lived. We went inside, and I had a seat, "I'll be right back," Wendy said as she went out of the door. I sat there waiting on her to come back. Wendy had just graduated and decided to sell drugs and live in one of the hardest projects in the city.

Finally, Wendy came back. "Erica, come in here and clean up this kitchen; you've got food all over this counter." Wendy had two daughters, Erica and Ashley; Erica was the oldest.

I decided to go outside. I stopped at Heather's house first, but she wasn't home. So, I strolled down by Lake Oaks, another housing project, right across the street from Techwood.

"Hey Eric," I called out as I saw him standing in front of the Lake Oaks projects while walking to the store.

"Come here; let me holler at you, folk." Eric was my cousin on my daddy's side. "What's going on with your cousin Wendy?" he said.

"Nothing, what do you mean?"

"Moe says she owes him some money, and he's coming up in there to take what she's got if she doesn't pay him."

"I don't know anything about that."

"Yeah, and I've heard she smokes, too, so you better be careful or go home. It's some niggas talking about coming up in there. You don't need to be up there, go home, Tosha".

"Eric, I don't believe that she uses drugs."

"Well, watch and see what happens," he said.

I walked away, stunned. How could Wendy be on drugs? She didn't act like it to me. Hmm... I wondered if I should call my momma.

I felt conflicted; Eric was not the type to make up a lie. I didn't want to call my momma because she'd get all hysterical and make me come home. I didn't want to go home, because my friends were here.

I went back up the street to Heather's house.

"What's up? What are we going to do today?"

Heather and I had been friends for about a year now. She was only a year older than me, but she didn't look like it. She also had a daughter that recently turned one.

Heather lived with her mother, father, two brothers, and an older sister. Her house was across the street from the Techwood Projects, so I went over there a lot.

"I don't know." she said, "Michael wanted me to go with him. Will you ride with me?"

"Who is Michael?" I asked her.

"Just this guy I met." She answered.

"Where are we going?" I persisted.

"I don't know, just go with me, please." She begged.

"Who's going to be with him? You know I don't play like that." I said, not wanting any trouble.

"Girl, it's not anything; we're just going to ride. Are you going or not because he's on his way?" She said, becoming agitated.

"Ok, I guess I can ride," I said, giving in.

Beep! Beep! We heard the horn blow.

"That's Michael," Heather said, "Come on."

We rode around for about 30 minutes, then Michael took us to some guy named Mark's house.

"What's up, Mark?" Heather said.

"Nothing much; who's your friend?" Mark said.

"Oh, that's Tosha," she replied.

"Hey, Tosha. How're you doing?"

"Hi," I said barrenly. I didn't want these guys talking to me.

"So, have a seat." We sat down on the couch while Michael and Mark started smoking a blunt.

"Girl, I'm ready to go. I don't want to be in here with them," I whispered.

"Just be cool. We'll leave in a minute."

"Hey Tosha, can I talk to you for a minute?" Mark asked me.

"What do you want?"

"I just want to talk to you," he said.

I turned looked at Heather, and she turned her head.

"I guess so," I said, not wanting to go.

He took me inside a small bathroom. "What side of town are you from?" He asked.

"No side," I replied.

"You're mean."

"No, I'm not. I just don't know you."

"Well, you can get to know me," he said.

I rolled my eyes to the back of my head. "I'll give you my beeper number," I compromised so that he would leave me alone.

"Ok then, I guess I'll have to take that."

"It's 615-8349."

"I'll page you tomorrow."

"Okay. Now, can you let me out of this bathroom?"

We left the bathroom, and Heather and Michael were in another room with the door closed. I went and sat back on the couch, but I was uncomfortable because Mark kept staring at me.

"Heather, I'm ready to go!" I yelled.

"Ok, here we come." She came out of the room, and then we left.

Chapter

2

It was 6 a.m. I woke up to see if momma was in her room, so I'd have a ride to school since the school was far away from our house. I looked in momma's room; she wasn't there. I went back to my room to wake up my sister.

"Hey, get up; momma's not here. How are we going to get to school?"

"I don't know. She hasn't been here all weekend."

"Dang, let me walk down to granddaddy's house to see if he can get us a ride or some cab money."

I quickly put on some clothes. Granddaddy only lived three houses down from us. He always kept us close because momma was on drugs, and she used to leave us by ourselves. Sometimes, she would be absent for weeks at a time.

Ring... ring...

"Granddaddy, open up!" I said as I was knocking on the door.

"What is it?" he replied. "Where's your momma?"

"I don't know. She's gone, and we don't have a way to school."

"Oh shit. Hell, I'm tired of this shit. Let me go across the street and see if Bonds will take y'all".

I stood in the living room as granddaddy walked across the street. He came back, "Bonds said he got an appointment this morning."

"So, how am I supposed to get to school!" I said, crying.

"Hell, I don't know!"

"I've got a test today, granddaddy! I can't miss my test!"

"How long has your momma been gone?"

"I don't know, I was up at Wendy's house this weekend, and I just came back last night. My sister said that momma hadn't been there all weekend."

"She's a hopeless case," Granddaddy said.

"I'm going to call Mr. Lord and see if he can come to get me." Mr. Lord was the principal at our school. He often had to take me home when momma was late or when she didn't show up to pick us up from school.

"Hello, Mr. Lord? This is Tosha. Can you come to give us a ride? I have a test today."

"I can't today, Tosha," he said. "Call Mrs. Jones. She'll give you a ride and tell her I'll take you home."

"Okay, thanks."

"What did he say?" Granddaddy asked.

"He said to call Mrs. Jones." Mrs. Jones was my teacher, but she was kind of like a mother figure. She would give me a ride and buy me clothes.

Sometimes, when momma didn't come home, she would take me to her house. But a lot of the time, I didn't want to leave my sister because I knew she wouldn't have a ride to school.

"Hello, Mrs. Jones?"

"Yeah, Tosha"?

"Can you give me a ride?"

"Where's your momma?"

"I don't know."

"Well, okay, I'll come to get you."

"Thanks, Mrs. Jones." I said, "Granddaddy, she's going to come to pick me up."

"Ok, I'll see if I can find your momma."

I went back home to get my sister up, "I've got a ride for us."

"Who?"

"Mrs. Jones is coming to get us."

"I bet she's tired of us," my sister said.

"Well, I'm not about to miss school, so are you coming or not?"

"Yeah, I'm coming," she said.

I was okay with going to school today because I knew I had a definite ride home. Sometimes, we would have to catch a cab. Then, my sister and I would get out around the corner so the kids wouldn't make fun of us.

After school, if momma didn't show up, we would catch a ride with Amy and Alex. Then, we would walk to Englewood to our Aunt Ester's house. Amy's mother, Sandra, and my momma were friends. She was our godmother, but we didn't see her unless they were getting high together.

Sometimes, if momma came in too tired, she would let me drive to school. One day, I drove and took Amy and Alex home.

***

"Tosha!" Sandra yelled, coming out the door. "Why are you doing driving that car? I can barely see your head over the steering wheel."

"Momma let me drive," I told her.

"I'm about to call your momma. She must be crazy. You're too little to be driving that car." She must have called momma because she was waiting at the door when we got home.

Let's just say I never got to drive to school again. When we were younger, and momma went to jail, Aunt Ester kept us until my sister got older and decided she wasn't going to follow Aunt Ester's rules. So, Aunt Ester took us back down to granddaddy's house. And like always, I followed her. I should've stayed with Aunt Ester; then, I wouldn't have to worry about how I would get back and forth to school. Instead, I stayed with my mother and my sister.

***

Finally, the bell rang. I sat outside waiting for my sister and Mr. Lord. My sister came out, "How was your test?" she asked?

"It was great. If I close my eyes while taking the test, then I can visualize the answers."

"Well, that's good," she said.

"Where's Mr. Lord? I wish he would hurry up."

Mr. Lord didn't always come right out. He had to do paperwork and stuff. Finally, after about 30 minutes, he came out.

I told my sister, "I don't know what's worse, waiting for him or momma."

"Me either," she said.

Once we got home, I went to see if momma was in her room. Again no sign of her.

"Is she in there?" My sister asked.

"No, I'm about to go down to sugar baby's house and look for her."

"You'd better not," my sister said.

"I don't care!" I yelled as I walked out the door headed down to granddaddy's house.

"Granddaddy, did you find momma?"

"Nope," he replied.

"She hasn't called, either?"

"No," he replied again.

"Okay, I was just asking. What's wrong with you?"

"I don't feel good," he said.

"Well, I'm about to call sugar baby to ask if she has seen momma."

"Hmm," granddaddy said.

"Hello, sugar baby? This is Tosha. Have you seen my momma?"

"Your momma was down here yesterday, but she left, and I haven't seen your momma since."

"Okay, do you have any idea where she is?"

"Nawl, baby, I sure don't," she replied.

"Well, okay, if she comes, tell her I'm looking for her."

"Okay, I will," she said.

After I hung up, I started thinking that maybe I should call the police and report her missing. It had been three days. Maybe something happened to her.

While I was in the middle of my thoughts, my beeper went off. The number read 622-5860. I wondered whose number that was. I decided to call and see.

"Hello, did somebody page Tosha?"

"Yeah, this is Mark."

"Oh," I said hastily.

"Can I come to see you," he asked.

"No, I'm about to go home to do my homework."

"You're still in school?" he asked.

"Yes," I told him.

"Oh, what grade are you in?"

"The eighth. Are you in school?"

"Nawl," he replied.

"Did you graduate?"

"No," he said shortly.

"Why not?" I asked.

"I got kicked out."

"You must be bad?"

"I guess so. Living the street life keeps you in trouble."

"I love school, I want to be a lawyer just like Matlock, and I watch it every day."

"Well, I hope you make it out," he said.

"How old are you?"

"Twenty," he said.

"Twenty! I'm only thirteen." I said.

"Well, we can be friends. Everybody needs friends, right?" he said.

"I guess," I said softly. "Well, I'm about to get off this phone and go home."

"Hey! When will I get to see you again?"

"I don't know."

"When is the next time you're going back over to Heather's house?"

"I may go this weekend."

"Okay," he said.

"Bye," I said and hung up.

I sat there for a moment, wondering what my next move would be. My aunt told me I would be a junkie like my momma, and I was determined not to be. She drilled that in my head, and it stuck with me.

A few of my mom's sisters were mean to us. One time, my aunt kept me while my momma went to jail.

***

"Hey! Auntie, it's my birthday," I said.

She smiled with a smirk, "Oh, it is," she said. She went into the pantry, got an oatmeal cake, and put a candle in it. "Here, happy birthday," she said as she laughed and walked away.

I was traumatized. *Why was she so mean to us? Why keep us if she was going to be mean?*

***

I was sitting on granddaddy's bed thinking about how I wanted my momma. Granddaddy came in from off the porch with Mrs. Frances and Gean.

"Get your ass off my bed," he said, "I don't know where your booty has been."

"Nowhere, granddaddy."

"So," he replied, "I don't like people on my bed where I have to lay my head."

I quickly hopped down to sit in the rocking chair.

I've got it! When granddaddy leaves the room, I'll call the police and report momma missing. I think I remember her tag number. I can give it to them and maybe they can find her. Yeah, that's what I'll do.

I sat there patiently waiting on granddaddy to go back outside. He and his friends would usually just sit on the porch all day. Finally, about thirty minutes later, granddaddy went outside.

I grabbed the phone. "911 Emergency".

"I want to report a missing person."

"Who is this?"

"Tosha Cook, my momma has been gone for three days."

"How old are you?"

"I'm thirteen, and my sister is fifteen. My momma's name is Martha Lewis, and she drives a blue 1988 Buick Skylark. The license plate number is HUL-156. She was last seen on Friday, but I can't remember what she was wearing."

"Are you and your sister staying at home alone?"

"Yes, my granddaddy lives across the street, and that's where I'm at now."

"What's your address?"

"Hell! Look it up on your computer. I've got to get off the phone before granddaddy comes in here. He'll kill me."

"Have you and your sister been without anything?"

"No, just find my momma; I've got to go!" I hung up as I heard granddaddy coming in from outside. I hope the police will find her.

I went back home to start on my homework. Once I had finished, I watched an episode of Matlock, then played my favorite Super Mario Brothers game. I only had three worlds left; then the game would be over. After playing my game for about thirty minutes, my sister came home.

"Here you go playing that stupid game again. Cut it off; I don't want to watch that game!"

I rolled my eyes into the back of my head. Then, I went into momma's room to continue playing my game. That was one good thing about momma being gone; I could have her room to myself. After about an hour of playing the game, I slowly drifted off to sleep.

Chapter 3

Whirl! Whirl! You could hear the police sirens.

"This is Officer Clarke, badge #23. I'm behind this blue Buick Skylark. The owner of this car was reported missing correct?" he asked.

"Copy, yes, Martha Lewis was reported missing yesterday by her daughter."

"I'm behind her now license plate HUL-156. I'm about to pull her over, copy," he said.

"Yes, officer, what is the problem?"

"Are you Martha Lewis?"

"Yes, why you ask?" she said.

"Well, for one, your license is suspended, and for two, you were reported missing yesterday. When was the last time you saw your kids?" the officer asked.

"I have been at my friend's house," Martha said, "they are old enough to stay by themselves. My daddy lives across the street from me."

"I know, your daughter called from your daddy's house."

"I'm going to beat her ass," Martha said to herself.

"Do you have ID on you?"

"Yes," she responded as she pulled the ID out of her purse.

The officer took the ID and went back to his car.

"I'm going to kill Tosha; I know her little ass is the one that called the damn police; now I got to deal with this shit."

The police officer came back to the car. "Can you step out of the car, ma'am?"

"What's wrong, officer?"

"Your license is suspended, and this is your second time getting pulled over." the officer said.

"Please don't take me to jail," she cried.

"Well, I may not, but what can you do to change my mind?" he asked.

"What do you mean?" she replied.

"You know," he said with a slight smirk on his face.

"I don't date officers, and I can't believe you would ask me something like that."

"And I can't believe a woman would leave her kids and not even call home," he replied.

"You don't know me, so don't judge me," she said.

"Look, either you're going to give me a date, or I'm going to take you in!" the officer said.

"What if I take your number and call tomorrow. I need to get home," she said.

"Okay, but if you don't call, I know where to find you. Since you don't have any license, I have an excuse to pull you over. Here is my card, and remember I work in this area, have a nice night." he said. Then he got in his car and pulled off.

"Tosha!" I heard momma scream as she walked into the house.

"Momma!" I yelled. I jumped up and ran out of the room, down the hallway to greet my momma. "Where have you been? I was looking for you!"

"I'm going to kill you. You had the police pulling me over!"

"I'm sorry, I was just worried about you. I didn't know where you were," I said while crying. "I thought maybe something had happened to you."

"I know, but I told you not to call the police. Where's your sister at?"

"She's in the room."

My sister came out of the room. "I don't know why you left her, knowing she's stupid. She calls everywhere looking for you," my sister said rudely.

"I know, I'm sorry. Momma, can I go over to Wendy's house this weekend?" I asked?

"No, you need to stay home."

"But why? All my friends will be up there, and it's fun up there."

"No, it's dangerous, and you don't need to be up there."

"Oh, momma, guess what. Do you know my cousin, Eric? He stopped me and said that Wendy was supposed to be on drugs. Can you believe that?"

"Yeah, I had been hearing that, too," momma said.

"I hope not. Maybe you and Kathy can go and talk to her. Eric said that she owed Moe some money, and he was going to come up to her house."

"Damn, I hope that girl is not on drugs," momma said, shaking her head.

"Yeah, momma, she might be," my sister said as she was coming down the hallway. "Last week, I went up there, and that refrigerator was bare. You know Wendy usually has a lot of food."

"Yeah, I know," I replied. "Well, momma, what do we do?"

"Let me call Kathy and see if she wants to go and talk to Wendy."

"Ok," I said as I walked down the hallway.

About an hour later, there was a knock at the door.

"Momma, somebody's knocking on the door!" I yelled from my room. I didn't feel like getting up.

"Oh, that's Kathy," momma said, "we're about to go up to Wendy's house."

"I want to go! I jumped up and grabbed my coat."

"Me too," my sister said. She jumped down off the bed.

Kathy was Wendy's momma, and she was on drugs, too. I guess it just runs in the family.

We forgave Wendy because there was a time when she was also mean to us.

***

One time she kept us, and her friends all took turns holding my sister down, whooping her for nothing. They held her down and were laughing as they took turns hitting her. I was too small to help her.

When momma came back, we told her, and she went looking for them, but she couldn't find her at the time. Then another time, we were with Wendy and our cousin Lisa, who was pregnant, when we got back to granddaddy's house. Lisa just got out of the car and started hitting my sister. This time, I was a little bigger, so I tried to help my sister. I got a mop off the back porch and hit Lisa in the head with it.

When momma came back, we told her what happened. We went up to Lisa's house, but we knew momma wouldn't fight her because Lisa was pregnant. We wanted revenge. That night we made a pact in the car to start fighting back since we are bigger now.

My momma was at the door talking to Lisa. My sister and I got out of the car and got some bricks. We threw them and burst her car windows.

"See, Martha," Lisa said as she walked towards her car. "They've busted my window!"

We got back in the car like we hadn't done anything. We decided to fight back. They weren't going to keep hitting us.

***

Within five minutes, we were at Wendy's house. The Techwood Project wasn't far from where we lived.

"Wendy!" Kathy yelled as she was beating on the door. Wendy came to the door.

"What happened to the living room suite?" I asked.

We walked into the house.

"Oh girl, I sold that shit," Wendy said. "I'm going to buy a new one, damn that shit," Wendy said.

We all walked in, looking around puzzled. There was no food in the refrigerator and no furniture.

"What's going on?" Momma asked Wendy.

"Nothing's going on; what do you mean?" Wendy said.

"We've been hearing that you're on drugs and owing people money," Momma said.

"Girl, I don't know what y'all talking about. I don't owe nobody nothing, and y'all don't need to come over here accusing me of the stuff, either." Wendy told her.

"We are not accusing you of anything. I'm trying to figure out what's going on." Momma said.

"Well, nothing is going on, so if you'll excuse me, I'm about to go lay down," Wendy replied.

"Well, let's go," momma said. So we all headed towards the door.

"She's lying," my sister said once we got outside. "Did you see that refrigerator?"

"Maybe she's not," I replied.

"You just don't want to believe it anyway," my sister told me.

"Whatever, you always think the worse of somebody!"

"Y'all quit arguing," momma yelled. "That's not going to help the situation. I'm going to call Marcus and see if he'll talk to Wendy."

Kathy started crying, "I hope my baby is not on drugs," she yelled.

Marcus was Wendy's baby daddy. They broke up after high school. He went off to a college out of town. Wendy abandoned her kids once she got on drugs. His mother helped out with keeping their kids. It was a long quiet ride home.

Chapter

4

It was Friday, and I was always glad when the weekend came because I could go to the Techwood Projects. I didn't have any friends in school, I mean, I had a couple of people that I ate lunch with, but that's all. All of my friends were outside of school.

It was my last year in middle school, and I sat there wondering what High School would be like. It seemed kind of scary to be going to High School. The only good thing was that my sister would be there.

This weekend I guessed I'd be at Heather's house since momma didn't want me at Wendy's house anymore.

Beep, Beep, my pager was going off. Hmm, I thought it was Mark and wondered what he wanted. I'd wait until I got out of school to call him back.

Finally, the last bell rang. I couldn't wait to get home to see if momma was there or not. Momma! I yelled as I walked in the door.

"Yeah?" she answered.

Good momma was there. It was always less stressful when momma was at home.

"I talked to Marcus," momma said as she came out of her room.

"For real, what did he say?" I asked.

"He came over here. I believe he was just drunk and hurt," momma said.

"Dang, why do you say that?"

"He was trying to have sex with me," momma replied.

"What!" I yelled.

"I think he is just hurt. I told him no and made him leave. Somebody called your granddaddy too, talking about Wendy has been selling her food stamps!" momma replied.

"That's terrible! Ok, I'm going down to granddaddy's house to use the phone." I said, leaving.

"Hey, granddaddy! Let me use the phone," I said as I walked into his room.

First, I called Mark back to see what he wanted.

"Hey Mark, this is Tosha. You paged me?"

"Yeah, what's up?"

"Nothing. Did you forget that I go to school?"

"Oh my bad, what are you going to do this weekend?"

"I don't know. I may go over to Heather's house."

"Well, if you go up there, can I come by there?"

"I don't know. I'll call you once I get up there."

"Ok then, cool."

I went back home to see if momma would let me go over to Heather's house for the weekend. When I got there, my sister was about to leave.

"Where are you going?"

"Over my friend's house," she said.

"Well, momma, can I go over to Heather's house?"

"No, stay home," momma said.

"Why?"

"Cause I want you to stay home this weekend," momma replied.

"It's going to be boring, I said sadly."

"Well, you'll find something to do," she replied.

I stormed to my room and turned on the TV to watch Matlock. After I got tired of watching it, I decided to play Super Mario Brothers. I had beaten all the levels, so I didn't know why I was still playing this game. I needed a new one. *I'll ask for one for Christmas.*

After I got tired of playing the game, I decided to go to sleep for the rest of the night. The next morning, when I woke up, Mark paged me. After I was up for about an hour, I went down to granddaddy's house to call him back.

"Hello Mark, you paged me again?"

"Yes, did you go up to Heather's house?"

"No, I'm at home. My momma wouldn't let me go."

"Oh dang, I wanted to come and see you."

"Well, maybe some other time," I replied. "I'll call you tomorrow," I said quickly as I hung up the phone.

I woke up the next morning, and both momma and my sister were gone. *I knew she wouldn't last too much longer,* I said to myself. I was home all alone. I got up and went into the kitchen to fix myself something to eat.

Let me see what I want. I opened up the refrigerator. *A bologna sandwich sounds good,* I said to myself. I pulled out the pack of bologna. After I ate, I sat on the porch for a while, waiting for momma and my sister to come back. As the sun started to come down, I was beginning to get worried. Neither my sister nor momma had come home.

I finally decided to walk down to granddaddy's house.

"Granddaddy, has my momma or sister called?"

"Nawl, why do you ask," he said.

"Neither of them has come home."

"Here we go with this shit," he replied.

I knew they weren't going to come home. Now I got to find a ride to school in the morning. I decided to call Mark; maybe he would give me a ride.

"Hello, Mark."

"Yeah, what's up? I've been waiting for you to call me," he said.

"Can you give me a ride to school in the morning?" I asked.

"Yes, what time?" He replied.

"At 7.30," I said.

"Ok then, I'll see you then," he said. He hung up the phone.

I hope momma doesn't come home now, I said to myself as I walked home.

Chapter 5

Beep! Beep! 6:30 a.m. sharp, the alarm went off. I woke up and looked around the house, but no one was home. There was no sign of my momma or sister. It was a good thing Mark was coming to pick me up to give me a ride to school.

At 7:00 am, I went to call Mark to make sure he was still coming.

"Hey Mark, are you still going to give me a ride?"

"Yes," he replied, "I'm on my way."

"Okay, I'll have the front door open."

I was very serious about school. If I finished school, at least I'd have a chance to be somebody. I was tired of being poor and dealing with this. School was my only hope. I went back home and stood at the door, waiting for Mark to come.

Beep! Beep! I hear a horn blow.

"Here I come," I said as I was locking the door. I jumped in the car.

"Hurry so I won't be late," I said. I buckled up my seat belt.

"How have you been doing?" He said with a smile.

"I'm okay," I said nervously. I was a little leery of him, but I needed a ride. Heather said she didn't think he would do anything to hurt me.

"I've been trying to catch up with you," he said, still smiling.

"I know, but since Wendy got on drugs, I haven't been able to get out much. My momma doesn't let me."

"Oh, where's your momma now?" He asked.

"That's a good question. I have no clue. Just get me to school."

"I know your cousin Wendy. She is always at some apartments called the Woodford Apartments."

"Oh yeah? So is it true that she's on drugs?" I asked him.

"Yes, she's out there," he said.

I fought away my tears. I hated that. I saw what drugs did to my momma, aunt, and father. Wendy was so young. She was only 22.

As we pulled up to the school, He asked, "What are you doing later?"

"I don't know," I replied, gathering my bookbag.

"Well, do you want me to pick you up?" he asked.

As I opened the door, I replied, "Maybe."

"Maybe?" he asked.

"Yeah, okay," I replied, "I'm sure I'll need a ride."

"Okay, then, see you later."

"Yeah, later," I said, then I closed the door.

The bell rang, I went into the class.

"Mrs. Jones!!!" I yelled, running towards her. I was so glad to see her.

"Where've you been?" I asked.

"Just working and out of town," she replied.

"I've been missing you," I told her. "I've been home all alone with no ride."

"Really," she replied, "Well, tomorrow I'll come to get you, and you can stay with me for the rest of the week. William is out of town".

William was Mrs. Jone's husband. He worked for TVA. They live in a big house in Hixson, and they didn't have any kids. I never asked her why. He sometimes traveled for work, and when he was gone, I got to spend the night.

"Are you coming to get me in the morning?" I asked.

"Yes, I'll pick you up for school. Tomorrow after school, we will go get our nails done. I was going to get you a starter jacket. It's a new coat everyone is wearing. Do you want that or the nails?"

I thought for a minute. Then I said, "Nails."

"Tosha, if someone asks you if you want a jacket or nails, don't be crazy enough to say the nails."

"Oh," I said, feeling dumb.

"But anyway, I was going to get you both. I was just trying to see what you were going to say." She replied.

"Don't be tricking me, Mrs. Jones," I said with a smile.

Thank God, I said to myself as I ran to my next class. I was so happy because Mark seemed creepy. I didn't like how he was looking at me. I mean, he didn't do anything out the way; it was just the vibe. Right now, I just needed him for a ride. Now I just had to get through tonight.

Chapter 6

I went outside looking for Mark. He had a yellow Cadillac, and I saw him parked over by the tree. I hurried up and got in the car before someone saw me.

"Hey," he said, grinning.

"Hi," I said shyly. I buckled up my seat belt.

"How was school?" He asked.

"Good," I said shortly.

"Dang, why are you so dry!" He said.

"I'm just tired." *I just want to get home without all the fake smiles,* I thought to myself.

"Oh, well, maybe when you get home, you should get some rest," he said.

"I will after I do my homework."

"I want you to hang out with me, but I know what you're going to say."

"Well, at least you know," I said with a smirk.

As we pulled up to the street, I thanked him for the ride.

"Call me anytime day or night," he replied.

"Yeah, okay," I said, getting out of the car. "See you later," I waved goodbye.

Whoooo, I dodged that bullet. Now I can be worry-free for a few days. I went into the house and flicked the light switch. *Aw, shit!* The lights were off. *Oh!!*

I ran down to granddaddy's house.

"Granddaddy!!" I said, running through the door.

"What is it?" he yelled.

"The lights are off."

"Aw, shit," granddaddy said. "Hell, I don't have any money."

"Well, I can't stay home in the dark. So, I'll have to stay with you in your bed."

"No, the hell you won't!" he replied.

"I'll call you a cab and go pay the light bill."

The EPB was on Highway 23. This wasn't the first time granddaddy had to put me in a cab to pay bills.

"Here's the money," he said with an attitude. "I'm going to find your momma and have a talk with her. I'm sick of this shit."

"Good luck with that conversation," I said as I walked out the door.

This is depressing, I thought to myself. Every day I was fighting to survive. What was my purpose on earth? All this worrying was wearing me out. I was just a kid. I desperately wanted to be able to take care of myself.

My sister had just got a job at McDonald's on Dayton Boulevard. They start hiring at the starting age of fifteen. Now she would be able to buy some of the things we needed. We needed a car, but my sister couldn't drive that well. She could drive a little bit, but I could drive better because I've had more practice. If we had a car, I could teach her.

Wendy used to let me drive. She would put me in her lap. Wendy had a friend named Brittany, and she used to take me driving as well.

***

When I stopped going to the Techwood Projects, Brittany would still come by my house to pick me up.

She had a 5-speed, but she still showed me how to drive it. If she came by and I wasn't at home. She would always leave a note.

"Sorry I missed you, kiddo."

One time Kathy stole a car and let me keep it.

"Here, Kemyatosha," that's what she called my sister and me. She always ran our names together. "Here are the keys to this car."

"Whose car is it?" I asked.

"Hell, I don't know," she said.

"I turned a trick last night. As soon as he went to sleep, I took his money and the car keys."

"What!" I said, making a face.

"Yeah," she replied. "Fuck him and feed him beans." That was her response to a lot of stuff. "Here are the keys," she said as she tossed them to me.

Kathy was hell! She was my mother's sister. My mother was number eight out of nine girls. Some of my momma's sisters were terrible and mean to my sister and me. Aunt Jackie hated my mother and took it out on us.

I remember this one time at my granddaddy's house; I was on the porch with Jackie and granddaddy's sister. I was about to go in the house, so I got up from the swing.

Jackie said, "Do you know that's not your real granddaddy?"

"What?" I said.

"He is not your mother's real father," she said and laughed.

"Granddaddy!" I said, running through the door. "Jackie said you're not my real granddaddy."

"Aw, shit," granddaddy said. He went to the door and slung it open. "Jackie, don't tell that girl that shit," he yelled!

"Well, you're not her granddaddy, and you need to tell her," she replied.

"Yes, I am," he yelled.

I was traumatized; I cried all night. I couldn't have been more than nine years old. Granddaddy had to rock me to sleep. My grandfather was my hero, and he was all I had.

"Don't worry about what she says," he told me. "I'm the one here with you. I took care of y'all. That's all that matters."

Kathy was dangerous. She carried knives and was not afraid to cut you. One time she and her daughter got into a fight. Kathy cut her from ear to ear. She almost died, but I'm glad she lived. I stay away from Kathy. I don't want her pulling that knife out on me. I knew if she would cut her own daughter, she would cut me, too.

One time, we timed her to see how fast she could get her knife out. She got it out in thirty seconds.

"How long I'm supposed to keep the car," I asked her?

"Hell, I don't care. Park it and leave the keys in it when you're done," she said.

"Okay, bye, Kathy."

***

In the middle of reminiscing, the cabman said, "We here."

"Okay, pull up to the drive-through window," I replied.

I would go through the drive-through. That way, they wouldn't see how small I was.

"Okay," the cab driver replied.

I paid the bill, and we left. When I returned home, I ran into granddaddy's house.

"Hey, I paid the bill. Any sign of anyone?"

"Nope," he said.

"In the morning, Mrs. Jones is going to take me to her house for a couple of days. I'll have a ride for the rest of the week. If momma comes, let her know."

"Okay," he replied.

"I'll call you tomorrow from over there."

"Why," he asked?

"You don't want to talk to me?"

"Hell no!" he said.

"Granddaddy, you're mean. I'll call you anyway." I walked out the door and left.

Chapter 7

When the alarm clock went off at 6:30, I jumped up out of bed. Today would be good; no worries. I got dressed and went down to granddaddy's house. I called Mrs. Jones to see if she was on her way.

"I'm on my way," she told me.

I went back home and waited at the door with my backpack. I also had my clothes for the rest of the week. She pulled up, and I headed out the door.

"Good morning," she said.

"Good morning," I replied.

"Have you had any breakfast?" she asked.

"No," I replied.

"Okay, we will stop at McDonald's."

After we left McDonald's, we headed to school. Once we arrived at school, I waved bye then ran to class. I forgot I was taking her class today, so I'd see her later. In eighth grade, we rotated classes and teachers. My teachers were; Mrs. Jones, Mrs. Cowman, and Mr. Cunningham for computers.

When school was finished, I was already waiting beside her car.

"I guess you're ready to go," she said, walking towards me.

"Yep," I replied. I couldn't wait to go to the mall and get our nails done.

"Where are we going first?" I asked her.

"Footlocker, we're going to get your coat first," she replied.

"Okay," I buckled my seatbelt.

When we got to the mall, I tried on several coats. We kept the one that fit me the best. It was a starter jacket that was silver, red and white.

When we left Footlocker, we went to the nail salon. Mrs. Jones would only let me get a French manicure. She didn't like for me to have color on my nails.

After we did our nails, we left the mall and headed to Mrs. Jones' house.

"You know which room is yours?" she said as she walked into the house.

"Yeah, I know," I replied.

Her house was huge, like a small mansion. She had three bedrooms upstairs and two downstairs. We always stayed upstairs. The house was made of brick, with a circle driveway in the front. She had a living room, dining room, den, and kitchen. She had plenty of space.

When the weekend was over, we packed up my stuff so she could take me home.

"Here is twenty dollars. I won't be able to pick you up in the morning, so just take a cab," she told me.

"Thank you very much for all your help," I replied.

"You're welcome," she said.

I got out of the car and went into the house and what a surprise. My momma and my sister were at home.

"Hey," momma said.

"Hey, I can't believe you're at home."

"Yeah, I'm going to try and stay around the house more." momma said.

"I hope so; that way, we can have a ride to school."

My pager went off; I looked at the number and saw it was Mark. I didn't have to call him since momma was home. I wouldn't need a ride.

"Momma, will you be here in the morning to take us to school?" I asked.

"Yes, I'll be here, I promise," she said.

"Okay," I said, not really believing her.

Now I had to hide the money Mrs. Jones gave me. I got out of the shower. I put the twenty dollars right at the top of the inside of my panties against my skin. Then I left out of the bathroom. If momma wasn't here in the morning, I would call a cab.

I went into my room to lie in my bed. I had a bunk bed, and my sister had a day bed. I always lay on my bottom bunk. Momma was there, so now I could get some sleep. I laid down and closed my eyes.

When the alarm clock went off, I jumped up and looked around. My sister was still asleep. I went into momma's room; of course, she was gone. It's okay; I had my twenty dollars. I went to the bathroom and pulled down my panties. The money was gone! *How did she go inside my panties, and I didn't feel it? How did she know I had money?* I began to cry.

"Tosha," I heard momma come through the door.

I opened the bathroom door and yelled, "Why did you take my money?"

"I'm sorry, Tosha, I'm going to pay you back," she replied.

"No, you're not!" I yelled. "That money was for me to go to school." I continued to cry.

"I know, that's why I came back," she said.

"Are you going to pick me up from school?" I asked her.

"Yes, I promise," she replied.

I stood there still crying.

"Tosha, I'm sorry, your momma needs help."

"Then why you don't get help then?" I asked.

"It's not that simple," she said.

"How did you know where my money was?"

"I could smell it," she replied.

"You could smell it?"

"Yeah, it's like I could sniff it out," she told me.

"That's crazy! How did you know she gave me some money?"

"I didn't. I told you it's like I could smell it. I'm going to pick you up and take you to school. I promise."

Chapter

8

When I got to school, I made sure to avoid Mrs. Jones. I was too embarrassed to tell her what happened. I'm glad I didn't have her class today.

When school was over, I ran outside. Great! Momma was here.

As I ran to the car, I yelled, "Hey, momma!"

"Hey, Shawty, I told you I was coming. I know you didn't believe me." She replied.

I smiled and got in the car. When I got home, my pager went off. I checked the number; it was Mark again. I thought about calling him back. I needed to keep him on standby. I might need him again.

When we got home, I told momma I'd be right back. I went down to granddaddy's house to use the phone.

"Hello Mark, you paged me?"

"Yes, how are you? I've been trying to get in contact with you," he said.

"I'm okay. I've been busy."

"I was trying to tell you something. I didn't know your sister was going with my brother Willie."

"How do you know?" I asked.

"My brother was telling me about her; then I realized it was your sister," he said.

"I remember her talking about a boyfriend. I just haven't met him yet."

"Yeah, she goes with my brother. He works at the KFC," he replied.

I wasn't surprised. My sister was boy crazy. Momma caught her with boys left and right.

I remember one day, momma brought her home and put her in the bed.

***

"Momma, what's wrong with my sister?" I asked.

"Nothing, she doesn't feel good," momma replied. "Sleep in my room today. Your sister needs privacy."

"Okay, I said." I loved sleeping in momma's room because she had a big queen-sized bed. She also had a little couch. It was big enough for me to lie on.

I went out of the room, and I peeked through the door. I noticed momma putting ice on my sister's breasts. Her breasts were swollen and leaking milk. I wondered what was wrong with her.

"Hey, mom, I'm going to run down granddaddy's house."

"Okay," she yelled from the other room.

I went down to granddaddy's house and asked, "What's wrong with my sister?"

"You know what's wrong with her," he replied.

"No, I don't. That's why I'm asking."

"She was pregnant. Your momma took her to have an abortion. I'm not paying for nobody to kill a baby. So I told Martha she had to pay for it herself. She needs to put that girl on birth control," granddaddy said.

"What's an abortion?"

"It's when they take the baby out of you," he told me.

"Then, what happens to the baby?" I asked.

"Hell, I don't know." Granddaddy said.

"Then why is her breast still leaking milk? I saw momma putting ice on it."

"I guess since milk was already in her breast, it had to come out." granddaddy said.

At the time she got pregnant, momma was off drugs and working the night shift. She came off of the night shift to watch my sister because she was buck wild. After that, momma got back on drugs. I always wondered if momma hadn't stopped working the night shift if she would've stayed off drugs.

***

"Hello," I heard a voice on the phone.

"Oh, hello Mark; I had drifted off in my thoughts."

"Oh, I thought you hung up," he replied.

"Oh no, just thinking to myself. Well, I better get back home."

"Okay, don't be a stranger," he said.

I told him I wouldn't; then, I hung up the phone.

Chapter 9

I went into the house to look for my sister.

"Hey, who is Willie?"

"Why are you asking me that?" she replied.

"I know his brother. He told me that you and Willie were dating."

"How do you know his brother?" she asked.

"I met him at Heather's house."

"Girl, you'd better not be talking to him. He is way too old," she said.

"Yeah, I know, but what about Willie?"

"What about him?" she replied.

"Well, is he your boyfriend?"

"Well, yes," she said.

"Oh, has momma met him?"

"She saw him once when she dropped me off to work," she replied, "Guess what, I'm saving up money for a car."

"That will be great," I told her.

The next few weeks went okay. I had to make an agreement with momma for her to stay around the house more.

One day, she came into our room and said, "If you don't want me in the streets, then I will have to get high at home. So you will have to stay in your room."

I agreed. I just didn't want my mother running around in the streets. It scared me. I remember one time granddaddy brought her home from the hospital with marks all down her arm.

***

"Granddaddy, what happened to momma?" I asked him.

"Well, she hitchhiked a ride, and the man tried to rape her. She jumped out of the car while he was still driving. She almost killed herself." he said.

***

Things like that gave me anxiety when momma was gone. That's why I agreed to stay in my room so that she could be at home. It was a love-hate situation. I loved her being home, but I hated the smell of the crack cocaine. Even though both of our doors were closed, you could still smell it in my room. It had a strong, distinctive smell.

The drugs made my momma very paranoid. Every time she would hit a piece, she would come into our room. Her eyes would be glassy, and she would say the same thing twenty times.

"Anybody messing with y'all? Are y'all okay?"

What I didn't get was when someone did mess with me, nothing was done about it.

***

I remember one day, my sister and my cousin Larry were at the house. Larry was my Aunt Kathy's son. He was twelve years older than I was. I think I was in-between the age of 9 and 11. I don't remember the exact age because I blocked it out.

Thoughts of this night sent me into a deep depression. At the time, my momma had a boyfriend named Luther. We lived on 12th street. My sister and I had been wrestling with Larry all day.

"Hey Larry," momma said.

"Watch them while I go to the store."

"Okay," he replied.

After momma left, he took us to our bedroom. We had bunk beds in our room, and my sister had the bottom bunk. Larry put me on the top bunk with him. I noticed he kept looking down at my sister on the bottom bunk. Then he put me on the side of the bed where I would be against the wall. He put his hand over my mouth. I made a confused look on my face. Then he put his hand in my panties. I started to kick and tried to scream. Why wasn't my sister helping me? I cried.

Momma came back through the door. He heard momma coming. He jumped down off the bed and ran past my momma out the door. I jumped down off my bed, running behind him and screaming. My sister ran into the kitchen behind me.

"What's going on?" my sister asked.

"Tosha, what's wrong?" momma asked.

Luther said, "What the hell is going on?"

"He put his hand in my pants!" I yelled.

"What!" momma said.

"Why you didn't help your sister? Where were you?" momma asked her.

"I heard her kicking, but I thought they were still wrestling," she said.

56

I was crying hysterically.

"I'm going to kill this motherfucker," momma said, "We will be back."

They left and when they returned she told me they couldn't find him. Then years later, momma told me that Kathy admitted to hiding him.

"I didn't want you to kill my son," Kathy told her.

I still wanted revenge, but a few years later, Larry went to jail for statutory rape. He was raped in prison. I remember the day he called granddaddy crying. I heard granddaddy telling my momma, but I didn't say anything. After what he did to me, they wouldn't mention his name around me anymore. I know it was wrong, but I was glad he got raped. He got what he deserved, but a part of me was still bitter because I didn't get my own personal justice.

Chapter

10

Christmas break had ended, and momma was back to her disappearing act. We had a bunch of presents under the tree before Christmas, but by the time Christmas came, I woke up with no gifts up under the tree. All of a sudden, my sister came through the door and saved the day.

***

"Tosha, look what I got you!" she yelled.

I jumped up off the bed. *Oh my God!* She had the 8 ball MJG cassette tape and a green, red, and blue eel-skinned pocketbook. I jumped for joy. She came through for me that day.

***

I walked to granddaddy's house so that he could find me a ride to school. Now I just had to find a way home.

"Hey, Mrs. Jones, can you give me a ride home today?"

"Okay, wait for me outside once school is over," she said.

"Okay, thanks."

She gave me a ride, and once again, she gave me another twenty dollars.

"Here, I'm off tomorrow, so use this money to catch a ride," she said.

Okay, this was like Déjà vu. I went into the house, and no one was home. I went into the bathroom and unscrewed the light switch cover. I put the twenty dollars in there. Now, this time she shouldn't find it.

Shortly after, my momma and my sister came home. We hung out in the kitchen for a little while; shortly after, we went to bed.

As soon as I woke up that morning, of course, momma was gone. I went to the light switch and opened it up. The money was gone! I stood there shocked; I didn't know what to do. I wondered if there were cameras in the house. How did she keep getting my money?

I give up. I didn't know what my purpose was in this life, but I wasn't about to live and find out.

The only thing I could do now was to kill myself. I'd fought all I could fight, but now I was tired. I went back into my room and lay on the bed crying. *How could I kill myself in the most painless way?*

I lay there thinking about what I should do. I decided to hang myself. Now, I had to find some rope. Today, I wouldn't be going to school. I didn't have the energy to find a ride. I went outside to the shed to find my jump rope, and I took it back into my room.

Hours later, momma showed up high. I always knew when she was high by how she looked and acted. She was in her room, and I was in mine. She didn't even ask why I wasn't in school. I went into the bathroom and shut the door.

I sat on the toilet, trying to talk to myself about hanging myself. It wasn't as hard of a decision as you might think. All I had to do was think of all the bad things I'd been through.

I tied the rope around my neck. I tied the other end around the shower rod. I stood on the edge of the tub, and then I stepped off. I must have made a sound once I stepped off the tub because momma heard me.

"Tosha!" she yelled.

I could hear her run through the house. She broke into the bathroom door.

"Oh my God, no!" she yelled.

She cried as she took the rope from around my neck.

"Oh my god, what's wrong with you?" she cried, "Why would you do this?"

She stood there holding me, crying. It was at that moment I realized my momma didn't even know how miserable I was.

Why didn't I try and kill myself when I was home alone? Did I really want to die? Did I want to be saved? I was caught in-between living and dying.

My momma cried for weeks, and she didn't leave the house. If she did, she would come right back. She even stopped getting high. Every time she looked at me, she would just cry.

It wasn't until then that I realized the Techwood Projects was my outlet. I had too much time to think and be miserable and depressed without it. As time passed, momma started letting me out of the house a little.

I went to Heather's house, and I rode around with Mark one day. We just talked, and he asked me a bunch of questions. Then, he took me back to Heather's house. At her house, there were no rules. We could come and go as we pleased.

I finally met Willie. He and my sister were about to go to the prom. She borrowed some money from granddaddy to buy her prom stuff until she got paid. Prom was right around the corner, just a few weeks away.

Chapter 11

When prom came around, my sister wore a black dress with pearl, cream, and pink stones at the neck. She looked marvelous. When she got paid that week, it was time to pay granddaddy's money back. She didn't have a bank account, so granddaddy would always cash her check.

"Granddaddy, here's the check," she said.

Granddaddy took the check and went into his room to get the money.

"Here, sign the back. So, I can deposit it into my bank account," he told her.

After she signed the check, he gave her the money.

"Wait! You shorted me a hundred and thirty dollars!" she yelled.

"Remember I gave you the money for the prom stuff. I just took it out of your check," he replied.

"Why!" she said, screaming.

"What you mean why? You said you were going to pay me back." granddaddy said.

"You took all my money," she said, crying.

"Aw, shit. Hell! You owed me, and stop all that yelling in my house." he told her. He turned and walked away.

My sister lost it. Granddaddy was closing the door that separated the kitchen from the front of the house. As the door was closing, she threw a knife into it. I stood there in shock.

Granddaddy opened the door back up, and he saw the knife.

"You threw a knife at me?" granddaddy asked her.

She just stood there looking.

"Get your ass out my house! And don't come back," he told her.

She stormed out of the house. Momma was walking down the sidewalk. "What's wrong?" she asked her.

"He took all my money!" she yelled.

"What money?" momma asked.

My sister threw the rest of the money she had in the street.

"What the hell wrong with you?" momma asked.

She ran into the house. Momma started picking the money up off of the street. Some of it went into the gutter, so it was lost. After momma got the money up, she went into granddaddy's house.

"What the hell is wrong with her?" she asked.

"She tried to stab me!" granddaddy yelled.

"What!" she said.

"I took the money from her check that she owed me, and she threw a knife at me. Come look," he told her as he walked towards the kitchen.

"Look," he showed her the knife in the door. "She can't come back to my house," granddaddy told her. "She has lost her damn mind!" granddaddy said.

From that point on, their relationship was estranged.

Chapter 12

I guess the effects of my suicidal attempt wore off. Now momma was back to her old routine. I was glad the school year was almost over. Momma was a no-show again.

Mark had been picking me up and taking me home. One time, he stopped over to his grandmother's house.

"Why did we come over here?" I asked him.

"I'm just running in there to get something," he said.

"Do you want to come in?" he asked.

"Oh no," I told him.

"Come in just for a minute," he said.

We went into the house, and I sat on the couch in the living room. No one was there but us. He went in the backroom then came back upfront. He sat next to me on the couch.

"Have you ever had sex before?" he asked.

"Hell, no! Why would I?"

"I'm just asking," he said.

"No, and I don't want to."

"Why not?" he asked.

"No point in it. I've got to make sure I make something out of my life. I have no interest in sex, and you're making me uncomfortable."

"Girl, I'm not about to do anything to you. Come on, let me take you home," he said.

I wondered if I didn't have sex, would he still give me a ride. For some reason, I felt like I owed him for his help. Next year I'd be going to High School, and I could ride the school bus. The bus stop was behind my house; so I shouldn't need his help. Would it be fair just to cut him off and not give him anything he wanted?

I didn't want to have sex, and I didn't want what came with it, like babies and stuff. I never thought about sex, and I didn't know much about it. I just knew I wasn't supposed to do it.

As the months went on, it was almost time for school to start. All Mark talked about was sex. I thought about doing it just so he would shut the hell up. I needed to ask Heather about sex. I didn't see her that much since she was going to Spain Park High school.

Finally, school started back, and I was in the ninth grade. I bought my school clothes and let Becky do my hair.

Momma had been over this man named Welford's house. He had been sending her to get drugs for him. He didn't know where to buy drugs or how much they cost. Momma had been beating him out of his money. She was getting hundreds of dollars at a time.

"Tosha! Wake up." momma said.

"What is it?"

"Here, take this money, put it up to buy your school stuff," she told me.

"Are you sure?"

"Yes, I'm sure," she replied.

Overall she gave me like five hundred dollars. I gave my sister half. Jazzy's clothing store was behind our house, and I walked over there and bought some clothes. I took my last fifty dollars to granddaddy's house to make sure momma didn't steal it.

"Hello," granddaddy said, answering the phone.

"Granddaddy give momma twenty dollars of that money."

"Okay," he said.

Momma went to get the money, but it wasn't me that called. Instead, it was momma disguising her voice.

The next morning granddaddy said, "Why were you up so late calling me?" he asked.

"I didn't call you."

"You didn't call me last night telling me to give Martha twenty dollars?" he asked.

"No, I didn't."

"That damn Martha! She called me playing like she was you and told me to give her twenty dollars," he said.

I'm not surprised. While the getting was good, she had been giving granddaddy money too. We were on a roll until momma told Kathy about her lick.

Of course, the minute Kathy got mad, she went and told Welford momma was beating him. He stopped giving momma money, and Momma believed he put a curse on her.

He used to have a pig head on his kitchen table with candles all around it. He would light the candles and chant over the pig head. Momma came home and woke me up.

"Look, this motherfucker cursed me," she said. She had a bald spot on the top of her head.

"Momma, I don't believe in curses."

"Look at my arm," she replied.

I didn't believe her until I looked at her arm, and you could see something crawling inside her skin. It scared me to death. I ran out of the house all the way to granddaddy's. After that, momma never went back to Welford's house.

Chapter

13

My sister finally got a car. It was a brown Toyota Corolla, a small car. It didn't really benefit me much, though, because she was letting Willie drive it, and when he wasn't driving, she was hanging out with her new friend, Mia. She was barely at home.

So even though I was not at Easton Middle School anymore, I still needed Mark's help a little.

"Come on, please," he asked me, "just to do it this one time."

He had come to pick me up from school again, I agreed.

"Only if there isn't someone at my house," I told him.

When we pulled up to my house, of course, no one was at home. So we got out, went into my room, and got on my bottom bunk.

"Hurry up," I told him, "before someone comes."

"I am," he said as he was taking his pants off.

He climbed on top of me and began to insert his penis.

"Oh goodness!" It burned and was hot.

"Stop!" I yelled.

"Wait a minute. I haven't put it in yet."

"No! Get off of me; this hurts," I cried.

"You got to get used to it," he whispered.

"No, the hell I don't," I said. I began to push him off, "Get up!"

He got off me and said, "You'll get to relax after you get used to it. It won't hurt like that anymore."

"Bullshit, I don't want to do that. I don't see why you like it. It feels horrible," I told him.

"After a while, it won't hurt anymore, I promise," he said, rubbing my head.

"Look, I don't want to have sex. I only did it to shut you up. Besides, I need birth control so I won't get pregnant. How can I get that? I can't tell my momma about sex; she will kill me."

"I can take you to the health department," he said, "I'm old enough."

"That's what you're going to have to do," I told him. But, whether he took me or not, I wasn't interested in sex. I just didn't like it.

The next few weeks went by kind of fast. I mainly rode the school bus to high school, and I would get off behind the red food store and walk home from there. My sister barely came to school anymore, and momma was out doing her thing.

"Don't talk to me about sex anymore," I told him. I didn't want to hear it.

A few months went by, and I started to feel sick in the mornings, every morning, I would vomit when I brushed my teeth.

"Tosha, what's wrong with you?" momma yelled from the next room.

"I don't know. I feel sick."

"You're going to the doctor," she said.

"Nah, I felt better after I vomit."

That evening when I got home, guess who was there? Wendy. Hey, I said, running to her.

"I knew you would be happy to see her," momma said.

Wendy looked bad. She had lost weight and had a black eye. She was so young to be going through that; she was only 23.

I found out she got on drugs because her boyfriend laced her weed one day. They called it primo. They were not strong enough for her, so she advanced to cocaine. I made up my mind that day I would never smoke.

"I went and got her," momma said.

"Oh, God," I said. Of course, I didn't mention the black eye.

My sister and Mia came through the door.

"Hey, Wendy," Mia said.

"What are you doing with Mia?" Wendy asked.

"She's my friend," my sister told her.

"Where did you meet her at? She's my age" Wendy asked.

"You know her?" momma asked.

"Yes, I went to school with her." Wendy replied.

"Let me talk to you," Wendy told momma.

We went into momma's room.

"What the hell is Mia doing over here? She's a dike."

"What?" momma said, "She just told me they were friends."

"Well, you better watch her," Wendy said.

After Wendy left, I went to call Mark.

"Where've you been hiding at?" he asked.

"Just at home; I've been feeling sick lately."

"Oh, yeah," he said, "how long?"

"For about a week or so," I told him, "I've been vomiting every morning."

"I bet you're pregnant," he said, laughing.

"What the hell? You must be out of your damn mind. I better not be. Why would you say that?"

"I'm a fast breeder; I'm fertile."

"That's not funny, don't play with me; I'll never talk to you again."

"You'll be mad if you're pregnant?"

"Mad?" I cried. "Have you lost your mind? I can barely get to school. I'm living in hell. What will I do with a baby?"

"I'll help you," he said, "and I'll make sure you finish school. I want a girl. I've already got two boys."

"Bullshit!" I screamed. "You'd better find someone to have you one. It sure as hell ain't going to be me!" I hung up; I was pissed.

He was playing, and it wasn't funny. Besides, I'd pushed him off, so I was sure I wasn't pregnant.

The next day in school, of course, I was sick again.

One girl said, "You vomit every morning; what's wrong with you?"

"I don't know," I told her.

Now I vomit after drinking milk. I went back to the bathroom. I was in my commercial cooking class. When I came out, this guy named Brandon was in my seat.

"Hey," I said, "I was sitting here. This is my stuff. I had put it down then went into the bathroom."

"Oh, I didn't know," he said.

"Man, you gonna let her move you out of your seat," a guy yelled from across the room, "I wouldn't get up if I were you."

"Please get out of my seat," I told him.

He sat there for a minute.

"Brandon, get out of my seat, please."

He still didn't move. I raised my hand back and slapped the dog shit out of him.

"Ohh!" the classroom yelled.

"Don't hit that girl," Mr. Cunningham yelled, "she's pregnant."

I hit him again then, Mr. Cunningham got in between us and broke the fight up.

On the way to the office, I asked Mr. Cunningham, "Why do you say I'm pregnant? Who told you that?"

"Why else would you be vomiting every day? It's morning sickness," he said, and he walked away.

Chapter 14

regnant lord Jesus, no! I called Mark.

"Hey, that health department you said you can take me to, can they tell if I'm pregnant?"

"Yeah," he said, "they do everything there. It's for people with no insurance, but I already told you are pregnant."

"Please, quit saying that." I didn't have the energy to get mad.

"Come take me," I said, "I'm sick as a dog. I'll skip school. I'll meet you at the auto zone behind my house."

"Okay," he said, "I'm on my way."

We got to the health department. They asked where my guardian was. Hell, I told them Mark was. They went over all the types of birth control and gave me bags of condoms. They also had me watching that video.

"Well, I won't need these condoms," I said, holding the bag, "Man, you're never going to try it again. Never!"

We waited in the hall because I wasn't on my period, so I had to take a pregnancy test before they would give me the Depo-Provera

"What's taking them so long?"

"I don't know," he said.

The door finally opened, and they came out three at a time. The lady was holding a bear with balloons in her hand.

"What's going on?" I asked, "Why you're smiling?"

'You're four months pregnant."

"Pregnant?" I Passed out.

"Get up, get up," they were saying.

I opened my eyes and saw Mark and the nurses standing over me.

"Tosha, are you okay?" Mark asked.

I said, "I just remember someone saying I'm pregnant."

"You are," she said smiling, and I began to scream.

"Stop hollering," Mark told me.

I couldn't stop crying. We got in the car, and I cried until my eyes were swollen.

"Stop crying. Listen, I'm going to help you," he said.

"I don't trust you," I told him, "You told me I wouldn't get pregnant. My life is already ruined. I can't believe this," I said, sobbing. "Just take me home."

When we pulled up at my house, I got out of the car, "I'm never talking to you again," I said, and I ran into the house.

I went into the house and went straight to bed. The next day I came home, and the house was full. My sister and Mia were in our room. They slept together on the day bed, and they seemed a little too close to me. I started to complain about them taking over the room. Plus, I had told momma about my sister not coming to school. So, momma wanted my sister closer to home.

"You can come into my room," momma told me.

A few weeks went by. Mark had been paging, and I wasn't thinking about calling him. I had a problem; I was beginning to show. My pants would no longer button. *Lord, what am I about to do now! I got it. I'll sneak some of my momma's clothes.* The next morning I was in the room with momma. The alarm went off, and I got up for school. I had put the clothes on momma's sofa. I sat down to put my shirt on. Momma was asleep. Soon as I pulled my shirt over my head, momma jumped up.

"Tosha, you're pregnant!" she yelled.

I didn't respond. I threw my clothes on and ran down the hall, and momma ran behind me.

"Are you pregnant?" she hysterically asked.

I kept running to the bus stop and never looked back. When school ended, I took my time going home. I didn't want to face my momma. I felt like I disappointed her. I didn't know what to say or do. When I came home, momma was in her room with the door closed. I went into my room and lay in my bed.

I noticed this briefcase sticking out from under my sister's bed. It had a combination lock on it. I picked it up, but it was locked. So, I put it down and stepped on it, and it popped open. I saw, 'I love you,' written all over the paper. I opened up the letter and began to read it. *Oh my God!* It was a love letter Mia had written to my sister.

"Momma," I yelled, running into her room. Look at this, I said, handing the letter to her.

"Wendy was right Mia is gay."

My momma read the letter.

"One pregnant and one a dike," she said.

She began to cry, then went back into her room. The next day after school, momma took me to granddaddy's house to tell him about my situation.

"I'm not paying for abortion," granddaddy said, "I don't believe in it."

"Please, granddaddy, I begged. I can't take care of a baby," I said.

"No!" he yelled. "I didn't pay for your sister's, and I'm not paying for yours. I'll help you take care of it," he said.

How could I reply to him? He was already old. He was 65 years old.

As we walked back home, "What're you going to do?" momma said.

"I don't know."

"What about the guy? Who is he?" she inquired.

"You don't know him," I told her.

"Will he help you?" she asked.

"I doubt it because he wants me to keep it."

"What about Mrs. Jones?" she said.

"I'll have to ask her," I said.

"I'm going to get off drugs," momma said, "y'all getting out of control."

When we got back home, my sister and Mia were there. Momma confronted them.

"Hey, are you and this girl going together?"

"No, momma," she said.

"I wouldn't be letting her stay here if I knew that. And you're too old," she told Mia.

My sister was going to be sixteen. They got into a big fight.

"Mia can't stay here anymore!"

"That's not fair," my sister yelled.

"Get out of my house."

"Why are you worried about me? Tosha's pregnant!" she yelled.

"Shut up," I told her. "At least, I'm still in school."

"I know she's pregnant," momma said, "but you not going to be in here with this girl." They both left, and Momma cried again.

Mark had gone to jail. He had someone to call and tell me. I didn't care. I was so mad at him. When he got out, he called. I finally replied.

"What?" I said.

"Dang, how long are you going to be mad? I was in jail, and you wouldn't write or nothing," he griped.

"So," I told him.

"Listen, I'm going to be here," he said.

"Shut up," I told him, "I don't want to hear it."

"When are you due?" he asked.

"In June," I said.

"Did you find out? Is it a girl?"

"Yes," I said.

"I knew it! I can't wait until she's here," he said.

"I'm glad you're excited," I said, and I hung up.

Chapter

15

"Tosha!" my sister yelled as she came through the door.

"What?" I said, getting up off my bed.

"That damn Mark, he isn't shit!" she yelled.

"What's going on?" momma said, coming out of the room.

"He got Willie to slap me," she screamed.

"What? What're you talking about," I asked.

"I was in Northern Park at a party, me and Mia. We saw Mark there, then he left and came back with Willie," she told us. "Me and Willie got into it, and he slapped me."

"But for what?" I asked.

"Because Mark told him I'm gay. I don't want you talking to him anymore," she said.

"How can I not talk to him, and I'm about to have a baby? Mark wasn't wrong; that's his brother. If I knew Willie was gay, I would tell you. What did you expect Mark to do?"

"I'm not gay," she yelled, and she swung to hit me.

I jumped up off the bed and hit her in the head with my shoe. My sister and I had never fought since we were young.

***

Sibling rivalry could be bad; they're not supposed to fight. My dad had killed his brother because they got into a fight. My dad picked up something and hit my uncle in the head with it.

He lived a few months and then died. I think they were fighting over drugs or money. My dad spent about five years in jail because they charged him with manslaughter. My momma forbade us to fight each other. She taught us to stick together and gang others.

I remember when my sister got into it with Arbor Place. They kept ganging us. One day, we were at the red food store. Some girls and guys from Arbor Place Projects tried to fight us. There were too many of them and they were bigger than us, too. My sister and I were very small, like 70 to 80 pounds. We went home and got momma. She came back to the store with us.

"Hey, what's y'all problem?" my momma asked one of the girls.

"Bitch, get out my face," she said.

"Bitch?" my momma replied, "oh, you got me fucked up."

The security officer came over and put us out of the store. We left out and crossed the street. Now, we were standing in front of the monument store.

"Wait till these motherfuckers come out," momma said, "I'm about to beat their ass."

They came out of the store, and we waited across the street. They came over. My momma asked the girl named Stacy, "Whom are you calling a bitch?"

"You," she said.

My momma hit her, and we all began to fight. I turned around, and my sister was fighting two girls; my sister held one, I had her hood, and the other one had her legs. I was very little, but my sister kicked one of them off. And she fell on the side of the car. I stomped her until both my shoes came off. She finally got up; she was big to be fifteen.

"Momma," I yelled.

My momma ran over there and said, "Bitch, you hit my shawty; I'm going to beat your ass."

"She stomped me!" she yelled.

So, my momma grabbed me by the arm, and we ran across the street.

"Where's your sister?" momma yelled.

"Here she goes," Crystal said.

Crystal was one of my momma's friends. She came over there with my momma, but she didn't help us fight. We were in the AutoZone parking lot. One girl picked up a garbage can, and she was going to throw it at my sister.

"Bitch," my momma said.

She hit her and shanked out her shirt. Her breast was swinging; her stomach looked big. My momma was running through all the girls. It was like four of them and two boys. I was just stealing them and running because they were too big for me to be fighting.

One guy told my momma, "I got a gun."

"You better use it then," my momma told him.

He never showed it, though. Next thing you know, Mississippi rode by and yelled out the window, "Martha, y'all better leave. Someone has called the police."

"Okay," momma said.

Mississippi was one of my granddaddy friends. We ran behind the AutoZone and jumped the gate to our house. We lived directly behind it in a duplex.

"Hurry up," momma said, pushing us through the door. Once we got home about an hour later, there was a knock on the door.

"Who is it?" momma said?

"This is Debra," she yelled, "Martha, you know me."

Momma opened the door. There, they were the kids we had been fighting.

"Martha, why is your grown-ass fighting my children?"

"Girl, these badass kids keep ganging my girls. I kept asking them to leave my kids alone. They're too little, and it's too many of them. So what the hell do they keep ganging my kids for?"

"I believe they were into it because my sister was friends with Benita. Then, she started talking to John, and he was going with Nikkie."

"Who were other friends of Benita?"

"So, she set my sister up to get ganged. That's what started all of this."

"I just went to talk to them," momma said, "then, one of them called me a bitch."

"They're all pregnant!" Debra yelled.

"Well, I didn't know, and besides, hell, they were messing with us," my momma said.

Granddaddy walked up. Mississippi must have told him because his car was down at granddaddy's house.

"Get off her porch," granddaddy said as he walked up. He was pushing the kids off the porch.

"I'm taking you to court, Martha!" Debra yelled, and she turned and walked away.

"Momma, you know them?" I asked.

"Yeah, she has been in the streets, too. She's on drugs also. She can take me to court; I don't care. I was defending my kids. I'm going to always defend y'all."

Chapter 16

It was just one of the many fights we had with Arbor Place. It all started when my sister became friends with Benita. She stayed in the street behind the projects. My sister had been hanging with her and started talking to John. He was going with Nikkie at the time, and that's where all the drama started.

They first ganged my sister in Arbor Place. Nikkie and Stacy. I believe Benita set her up. At the time, my cousin Venus from Alabama came here to stay with my Aunt Liz. Venus was two years older than my sister. She was my Aunt Gwen's child. Venus came here to go to summer school at a high school for the summer. Liz stayed off Highway 58, so it was a good way from where we lived.

Someone called granddaddy's house and told me my sister had got ganged. Dang! Momma wasn't there, so I called Venus.

"They ganged my sister in Arbor Place," I told her.

She had already heard about the beef.

"I'm going out there and beat their ass," she said.

"How you're gonna get there?" I asked her.

"I'll catch a cab."

"Who's gonna pay for it?" I said.

"Hell, I don't know," she replied, "but I'm not going to leave my cousin out there alone. I'll meet you there." She hung up.

I guess I'd walk to Arbor Place, it wasn't far, but it was a good walk. The fight would be good and over by the time I got there.

I left a note for momma telling her what happened and where I was. I made it just past Orchard Park and by Wilson Street.

I saw momma ride past me flying. I tried to flag her down, but she didn't see me. When I finally made it to Arbor Place, momma and Kathy were there. I saw the cab driver waiting for Venus, I guess. They were all in the street yelling and cursing.

"You got her fucked up," my momma yelled.

"What's going on?" I asked.

"Nothing, get back Shawty," momma yelled, "I'm going to beat all their asses about my daughter."

"No, let me get them," Venus said.

Of course, the police came, so we left. The cab driver followed us to granddaddy's house.

"What about the cab?" I asked Venus.

"Hell, I don't know," she laughed.

"Just go and ask daddy," momma said.

"Granddaddy, we need money to pay for the cab."

"Hell, I don't have money," he yelled. Well, he's out there waiting, I told him.

"He's not gonna leave until I pay him."

"How much is it?" he asked.

"Thirty dollars," I said.

"Thirty! What the hell!" he shouted.

"She got into a fight," Venus explained, and I had to go to help her.

"Bullshit!" he said, "don't you do that shit anymore."

The next fight, Venus instigated. She called Benita's phone and played on it until they came around granddaddy's house.

"I didn't get to kick their ass," she explained, "I'm gonna get them."

She made what she called her secret potion on the back porch.

"Come out here, look at this shit," she said.

She laughed and clapped her hands; she was always laughing. My sister and I came outside, and Venus had a cup. She was pouring bleach, peroxide, ammonia in this cup, and it was popping, and the smell was awful.

"What's that?" I asked. "When they come, throw this in their eyes," she suggested.

"No, You're going to kill somebody," I told her.

"Hell, if they come here, they need to be killed," she said, laughing.

If granddaddy sees this, we're going to get in trouble.

"He won't see it," she said, "we're leaving it on the back porch."

Momma and Kathy walked up.

"What yawl doing?" they asked.

"Oh, nothing," we replied.

They went into the house. Then, a few minutes later, came Benita and her crew.

"No, you motherfuckers didn't," momma said, running out the house, not knowing Venus called them.

"This is what I been waiting for," Venus said. She jumped off the car. "Which one of yawl wanna fight?" she asked.

"I'll fight you," Richard said, and he hit her and ran. Venus chased him. My sister was standing there with the cup in her hand, while Momma fought two girls in the street.

"Throw the water in my eye," Felicia said.

Water, I'm thinking? She doesn't see all that stuff popping out of the cup.

"Throw the water," Kathy yelled from the background, "and sprang on that bitch!"

"Throw the water," Felicia said again. My sister finally threw it.

"Finish her off!" Kathy yelled, "Break the cup on her head!"

My sister did. Felicia screamed.

"I can't see, I can't see," she said.

Benita came from across the street and walked away with her. Venus came running back down the street.

"What happened," I asked. "That nigga hit me and ran. I chased him to the red food store and hit his punk ass back in the head with a bottle. He got me fucked up."

This was a hot mess, and things were way out of control. Let's say it was the last fight we had at Arbor Place.

Chapter 17

This incident landed us in court. Felicia was almost blind in one eye, and she had been wearing a patch. By the time we went to court, Venus was gone back home. I hate to say we were glad when she left. She was getting us in all kinds of trouble.

Venus was bad as hell and too wild. One night she kept complaining; she wanted some chocolate chip cookies.

"Walk to Pruett's with me," she said, "I want some cookies."

"The store's closed," we told her.

So she said, "I'm going to bust the window."

"Yeah, right," we said, and we laughed.

She walked over there. We went with her we wanted to see this. This fool walked up to the store window and threw a brick at it. The alarm went off, we ran. Of course, as always, we were laughing.

Another time we wanted to go to a party at the National Guard Armory;

"I know how to steal a car," Venus told us.

Of course, like dummies, my sister and I followed her. We went like two streets over to Cleveland Street. It was an old brick parked in the street. We tried the doors; it was unlocked. So my sister and I got in the back seat, and Venus got in the front.

"I know how to hotwire a car," she said.

We didn't think she really could do it. We sat in the back seat while Venus messed with the wires. Lord, the car started up. Venus began to drive down the street. My sister and I turned and looked at each other in shock. As soon as Venus got to the next stop sign, my sister and I jumped out and ran. Venus parked the car in the middle of the street and ran behind us.

"Where y'all going?" she asked as she laughed and clapped her hands.

"Home!" we yelled over our shoulder, "you're crazy."

The last of the Venus events were we were all bored one day, and we went 'nigga knocking.' Knocking on doors and running. Again we were like two streets over. We were knocking on people's doors and running and laughing.

Well, word must have gotten around about what we were doing because the next thing you know, we knocked on this door. The man on a cane yanked the door open.

"Y'all better not knock on my motherfucking door!" he told us, "I'll beat y'all ass."

We were stunned. We struck out running, and the man chased us. This old man with a cane almost caught us. I was terrified.

"Hurry up!" Venus yelled.

"I'm tired. I can't keep up," I cried.

She and my sister grabbed me by the arm and pretty much dragged me home. I told Venus never again. I wasn't going anywhere else with her. Before Venus left, of course, she had to do something else.

Granddaddy was renting his backroom to a lady named Bernice. We couldn't stand her. She was mean.

"I'll set a trap for her," Venus said.

"What kind of trap?" we asked her.

"I'll show you," she said.

She tied a string from the door to the porch rail. "Look, when she opens the door, she's gonna slide and fall down the stairs."

"Oh, goodness," I said.

"It's just a little fall," Venus said.

"She won't be hurt bad," she said, laughing and clapping.

The problem came as the next person to open the door wasn't Bernice; it was my momma. She slid clean down the steps to the floor!

"Tosha and Venus!" she yelled.

We all ran outside.

"What the hell y'all doing tying this rope?" she yelled. "I fell and almost killed myself," she said, looking right at me.

"Why're you looking at me?" I asked.

"I know your little ass did it," she said.

"No, I didn't," I said, but I didn't say who did.

"Well, who did it?" she asked.

We all just stood there.

"I'm getting you!" she yelled.

She got up and popped me a couple of times.

"Now get this shit up," she said and slammed the door.

"I'll help you," Venus said.

I just rolled my eyes. She helped me take it down. That was the last summer Venus spent with us.

Chapter

18

Now it was time for court. We walked into the courtroom, and Felicia and their crew were already there. It was just me, my momma, and my sister. Venus stayed in Alabama; she didn't come. They were mean, mugging us when we walked in. I just ignored them. I always felt safe with momma because I knew she wouldn't let anyone hurt us even if it cost her life.

The district attorney put my momma on the stand.

"Let me get this straight, you 35-year-old fighting 15-year old children," he said.

"Yes, my momma answered, "but I didn't know how old they were, and they were fighting my kids and me. There were seven of them; what was I supposed to do to protect my kids?" she asked.

"I don't know," the DA said.

"Why you didn't call the police?"

"We were walking home, I didn't have a phone, and they cursed and hit me. I have the right to defend myself and my kids," she told him.

After the judge listened to all the evidence, he made his ruling.

"I see no reason to prosecute Mrs. Lewis. She was only trying to defend her kids. She acted rightfully in self-defense. As far as the bleach incident, they came to their house—something you should never do. So I'm dismissing all the charges. And Mrs. Lewis is not required to pay any medical bills. Now I'm telling both of you, stay away from each other." The judge warned, "You need to have no contact period, or I'm locking y'all up. Case dismissed." The court adjourned.

"Come on," momma said.

A big black girl followed us as we walked out of the courtroom. We made it to the bottom steps, and there she came.

"You ought to be ashamed of fighting those kids!" she yelled.

"I'm 25; fight me," she said.

103

"Bitch, you don't even know me!" my momma yelled. "But bring your ass down here, and I'll beat your ass, too," momma told her.

By this time, the security guard came outside and made her go back in.

"That bitch doesn't know me," momma said as we walked home.

That ended the Arbor Place feud. I was glad.

Chapter 19

After hitting my sister in the head, we began to fight down the hall.

"No!" momma yelled and cried. She broke us up.

"If you talk to him, I'm never talking to you again," she threatened, then she left.

It was the turning point for my sister and me; we were never the same after this point.

Since I'd been in high school, I hadn't talked to Mrs. Jones much. I missed her. Maybe after school, I'd go to see her.

When school was over, I got a ride to Easton Middle to see Mrs. Jones. High school got out before middle school. I ran around the back directly to her room.

"Hey, Tosha," she said as she ran up and hugged me. "How you been doing?"

"I'm okay," I told her.

"Are you pregnant?" she came right out and asked. I was stunned.

"How do you know?" I asked her.

"Your sister called and told me."

"She did?" I replied.

"Yeah," she said.

Why would she do that? I said to myself.

"I can't believe you're pregnant," Mrs. Jones said, "and especially by that old man."

"Yeah, I messed up," I told her.

Damn, my sister told everything, and why was she telling my business before I could? That pissed me off.

"Well, you'll be okay," she said, "come on, let me take you home."

I got home, and granddaddy was extremely excited about the baby. I didn't know why.

"Here, I cooked. You've got to eat and feed my baby." He was making sure I ate well every day since I was pregnant.

He and Mark were happy. I was ready to shoot myself, and momma was always crying.

I finally talked to Mark, I'd be having the baby soon, and it wasn't like I had any money.

"How have you been?" he asked.

"What happened with you, my sister, and Willie?" I asked him.

"Man, that bitch gay. I was riding through the Projects and saw her at a party full of dikes. So, I went to my brother, they got into it, and he smacked her."

"Well, she got mad at me," I told him.

"What is she mad at you for?" he asked.

"I was wondering the same thing. She doesn't want me talking to you. She feels like you're starting trouble for her."

"Man, how am I starting trouble for her? Mia is a known bull dyke; everybody knows her and knows she's gay. You don't need to be in this," he said.

"Well, she has put me in it, and she forbade me to talk to you."

"That's bullshit. What are you going to do?" he asked.

"I don't know," I said. "I've got too much on my plate to be worried about this."

"Let me come get you and see you," he said.

"Not today," I replied, "maybe another day," I said, and I hung up.

I hadn't even told Heather I was pregnant; she would have died.

"Hey, Heather."

"Hey, girl, where have you been?"

"What have you been up to?" I asked her.

"Nothing. I started at Spain Park High this year."

"Oh really," I said. "Can you come to pick me up? We need to talk."

"Okay," she said, "I got my brother's car."

She came right over, and we got in the car. Before we made it to the end of the street, I opened my coat and put her hand on my stomach.

"Bitch, you're lying!" she screamed. "Tosha, I know you're not pregnant."

"Yes, I am," I said sadly.

"Girl, why you haven't told me?" she asked.

"I've been going through a lot," I told her.

"Dang, I can't believe this," she said.

"What did your momma say?"

"Just cried," I replied.

"I hate that you're pregnant by Mark's ass. He needs to know that diapers are going to come before that powder."

"What powder?" I asked.

"You didn't know," she said. "He and Michael snort cocaine."

"Girl, hell no! Why didn't you tell me that?"

"I thought you knew," she said.

"Oh goodness," I said. "Well, I'm not relying on him anyways. Granddaddy said he's going to help me."

"I hope he does," she said.

"Having a kid is hard; I don't know what I'd do without my parents," she said.

"Yeah, I know," I replied.

We pulled back up to my house and said our goodbyes. I promised to keep in touch. I waved at her as I walked into the house.

Chapter

20

Back at school, everyone knew I was pregnant. In a way, I was glad because I didn't have to keep hiding it. I cried every day, and I had to talk to myself out of bed. I was so down I knew I wouldn't be able to be a lawyer now. I ruined my life. I no longer cared about my appearance, and I rarely combed my hair. I was standing in the lunch line.

"Hey Fantasia," I said to one of my friends.

"Hey Tosha, how are you doing?" she asked.

"I'm okay," I said.

"Your sister told me you were pregnant."

"Oh, did she?"

"Yes," she said. "And she told me she wasn't going to help you with the baby."

"Really, why would she say that?"

"I don't know," she replied.

"She needs to shut the hell up," I said as I walked off.

She's going to make me curse her out, I said to myself. *How is she mad at me about something I didn't have anything to do with?*

When school let out, I was walking home from the bus stop. When standing at the stop sign, I saw my cousin ride by. She was my aunt's daughter. She looked at me at the stop sign and just kept on driving.

"Damn," I said. She didn't bother to ask if I needed a ride or anything.

They are so low-down. My momma's sister hated her, and it showed. They were so jealous of our relationship with granddaddy, and her resentment made her poison her kids and a lot more of the family.

When I got home, I stopped at granddaddy's house. "Your food is on the oven," he said as I walked in.

"Okay," I yelled.

He was on the phone. I heard him say my name, so I went into the small room next to his.

I heard Jackie say, "Marissa saw Tosha at the bus stop, and she said she looked bad."

"No, she didn't," granddaddy said.

"Well, Martha is her momma," Jackie said, "so what can we expect from her."

"She will be alright," granddaddy told her.

All they do is talk about people. Why would she do that? She was old enough to be my mother. Okay, they want to say what I'm not going to be. I'll show them. I didn't know what I was going to be, but I knew I was about to fight like hell.

I finally met up with Mark; there was no need to keep dodging him. I'd be having the baby soon. I had to think of a name for her.

"Hey," he said, smiling.

"Hey," I told him.

"It's so good to see you," he said.

Of course, I didn't respond. He took me up to his grandmother's house. She stayed in Heritage Park up a big hill. Of course, he wanted to have sex. I didn't want to, but I guess it didn't matter now that the damage was done. I still had no interest, so I just lay there.

When we finished, I went and sat on the living room couch. Then his uncle came.

"Hey, Tosha, this is my uncle," he said.

"Hey," I said shyly.

His uncle was looking at me, making faces. He was creeping me out. Mark went outside to smoke a cigarette.

"Hey Tosha, come here for a minute," he said.

What does he want? I was thinking. He took me into one of the bedrooms and locked the door.

"Take down your panties," he said.

"What!" I yelled.

Mark came bursting through the door.

"What y'all doing?" he asked.

"He told me to take down my panties," I said, crying.

Mark sprang on him, and they began to fight all the way out of the front door to the porch. Once Mark got him outside on the ground, I looked in my purse and saw the $70 Mark had just given me was gone. So I went to the porch.

"He took the money you gave me," I said.

Mark went into his uncle's pocket and took everything he had. Then, he came back into the house and gave me the money. I couldn't stop crying.

"Calm down," he said, "I'm not going to let anyone hurt you."

"Take me home," I yelled.

"Okay, I am," he said.

"Are you going to pay me something for getting your money back?"

"What?" I said. "Boy, fuck you! You gave me the money now you want some of it back? Hell, no! He was probably going to rape me. You got me up here with this creep and then think I'm going to give you something. I'm not giving you shit!" I said.

"Come on," he said.

He took me home, and I just cried. Why did this keep happening to me?

***

I remember one time I was in the Techwood Projects walking around at night. This guy named JR was like, "Hey Tosha, come here."

"What?" I said.

"Let me show you something," he said.

He took me behind the building.

"You gonna give me some pussy?" he said.

"What!" I said. I was confused.

Then my cousin Eric came around the corner.

"Hey man, what are you doing?" he said.

"Nothing," JR told him. "I was just talking to her."

"No, he wasn't," I said. "He's asking for sex."

"Hey, man, that's my cousin; leave her alone."

"Come, on Tosha," Eric said, grabbing my arm.

Lord, he saved the day.

"Don't be walking around out here at night," he said.

"How did you know I was back there?" I asked.

"I saw you when I was coming up the hill," he told me.

"Thank God, you did," I said.

"That's why I've been telling you to stay home," he said.

***

And now here we go, the same scenario again, Déjà vu.

Chapter

21

Of course, now I'm never going back up to his grandmother's house again. It's almost time to have the baby, and I have no idea what to name her. When I came home from school, my sister was there. I hadn't seen her in a while and didn't want to see her. We just walked past each other in silence.

Finally, she asked, "When are you going to have the baby?"

"June," I said.

"You have a name?"

"No," I responded. "I'll have to think of something."

"You want me to name her?" She asked.

"I don't care," I said.

"This is one thing I hate the most about the family; they skip over issues. They don't resolve anything," I said.

Why was she talking to me like nothing happened? I wasn't going to use what little energy I had to fool with her. I had to stay focused. I was working on a plan.

Today, I went to the doctor. My doctor's name was Dr. Martin, and I hated his office. It was super ghetto and always crowded. I had to wait hours in the front and the back.

"Hey, young lady, how're you feeling?" The doctor asked.

"I'm okay," I said. I loved my doctor because he was so nice, and didn't make me feel ashamed of being pregnant.

"You're a 105-pound sister," he said. "I believe this is about the biggest you're going to be in your life. So you're ready to have this baby?"

"I guess I have no choice."

"You'll be alright," he said, smiling. "Call us if you need anything," he said and walked out the door.

His office was right in Heritage Park, on Wilcox Blvd. He was right by Mark's house within walking distance. Sometimes, I would walk up his house if I didn't have a ride home.

A few weeks later, a few of my friends decided to have a small baby shower for me down at granddaddy's house. My friend Nicole organized it.

"Granddaddy, can I have a few friends over for a shower?" I asked him.

"Sure," he said, "I'll cook for you." My granddaddy was a cook. He owned a restaurant on 9th street called Fish and Chicken Box. When my momma was younger, she used to work there, and so did his sister.

I just had a few friends over, Nicole, Renee, Shun, and a few more girls. There were about seven of us. We ate, laughed, and talked. It was the only happy moment I had during my pregnancy. They gave me a lot of small stuff; diaper bags, bottles, bibs, wipes, things like that. I was appreciative.

I only had a few months left in school. I was so big I was about to pop. I was sitting and wobbling alone.

The next day in school, I was in my math class. Mrs. Ross was my teacher. My friend Brittany came rushing in, "Tosha, they about to gang your sister in the hallway."

"What!" I said.

I jumped up and ran down there, and the hallway was full. I was pushing my way through the crowd looking for my sister. I finally saw Mia.

"Hey, what's going on?"

"They got me fucked up," my sister yelled!

"Who?" I asked. It was so many people.

"These hoes," my sister yelled. Nobody was hitting her, though.

"She's alright," Mia said, "Nobody gonna mess with her."

"I know they won't," I said. I reached in my bag and got my mace, and started spraying. I sprayed the whole hall. People were running and choking, including me. I wasn't about to fight while pregnant, and even though my sister and I were having issues, I knew momma would expect me to help her. I couldn't let her get ganged. Of course, they took us to the office.

"Tosha," the principal said, "I'm tired of you. To be a little pregnant woman, you sure are causing a lot of trouble."

"No, sir," I said, it wasn't my fault.

"Your grades are good," he said, "but mace is on the zero tolerance list. So I'm going to put you out. Since you're pregnant and there are just a few months left, I'll allow you to be home schooled. But don't come back next year. As for your sister, how did you come in here with someone that graduated years ago for a fight? You're barely coming to school anyway, so I'm putting you out. And don't come back next year, either. You also will repeat the 11th. You haven't come to school enough to pass." He told us. Then he walked out.

Chapter

22

Of course, momma wasn't mad about school since I was defending my sister. She liked for us to stick together. I was kind of glad to be out of school; I had been hurting so badly. The teacher had been coming to the house once a week, so I kept up with my work.

Next year, I think I'd go to Bob Jones High School. It had a bus that came behind granddaddy's house. I knew my sister was glad to be out too. She wasn't going to school anyway. She kept saying she wasn't going back next year, but I told her to go to Bob Jones High with me. I don't know if she will because she wasn't interested in school anymore; I didn't know why. She was really smart and very creative. She could draw, make stuff, and fix hair. I couldn't do none of that.

Granddaddy came down to our house. I wondered what he wanted. He never came down here.

"Hey, Martha, let me talk to you. You see that house," he pointed across the street, "the old man that lived there has died. His family's selling the house for ten thousand dollars. I'm going to buy it and remodel it for you and the girls."

"That's a shack," I said. The house looked disgusting. It was dirty, with no windows, and it was built in 1927. It was what they called a shotgun house. "You walk straight through it, no turns," I said.

"I'm going to remodel it," granddaddy said.

"It seems so small," I said.

"No smaller than where you live now," he said.

"Well, that's true," I said.

"Plus, with you're having a baby, I need y'all to be close to me so I can look after y'all. So, Martha, what do you think?" he asked.

"That would be great," she said, smiling for me to own a house. A tear came down her eyes.

"Well, come on over here. Martha, and let me show it to you," he said.

We walked across the street, and granddaddy showed me the house and told me his plans. I watched from the door.

Momma returned very excitedly, saying granddaddy would sign for the house this week since she liked it.

She said, "By the time you have the baby, we'll be moving into the house across the street."

I didn't care anyway. The next few weeks went by pretty quickly, and my sister had only come through a few times. She told me the name she came up with for the baby, but I couldn't remember. Granddaddy had been having people working on the house. He came to get momma like every other day to show her things they had done. It was the happiest I'd seen her.

I talked to Mark a few times, but, of course, I hadn't been back up there.

One morning momma got up early to go down to granddaddy's house. "What's wrong, momma?" I asked.

"Sherry left Walter in the North side," she said, "He's walking around by himself. Someone called and told your granddaddy I'm about to go and get him." Sherry only had one son. In a way, I felt bad for him; then, in another way, I felt like we were barely making it, and she didn't have room to try and help someone else.

Momma came back with Walter. Walter and I were three years apart. He was going to a middle school around the corner. He slept on the top bunk in my room, and I mainly slept in my momma's room while she was spending most of her time running back and forth to the house.

The next morning my stomach was hurting so bad.

"Momma," I said, rocking her. "Get up. I need to go to the hospital. My stomach is hurting so bad."

"Are you bleeding?" she asked.

"No, but I'm hurting so bad."

"Okay," she said. So she got up and went down to granddaddy's house. He called us a cab.

"Make sure Walter gets up for school," she told him.

"Alright," granddaddy said as we got in the cab.

Once we got to the hospital, they called my regular doctor. Then they started running some tests.

"Looks like you're trying to go in labor," Dr. said. "I wish you would wait," he told me.

"But I'm hurting," I said.

"I know, but you're pregnant, so I need to be careful what I give you. First, let me do the test to see if her lungs are developed."

They took me into the room and put me on the table. Then, they pulled out this long needle.

"What are you about to do with that?" I asked.

"We're going to stick it in your stomach to check the fluid."

"Like hell, you will!" I said. I started to try and get down.

"Be still," he told me.

The baby just didn't like that. The minute he stuck that needle down in my stomach, she started kicking me and going crazy. I let out a scream. It hurt so badly.

"Calm down," the doctor said.

"It's hurting," I told him.

They put me in a wheelchair and gave me some medicine. If this is just a test, hell how could I make it through labor? They put us in a room while we waited on the test results. After an hour or so, he came in.

"Well, her lungs are not developed enough for me to induce you. So I'm continuing your bed rest."

"Okay," I said. I wasn't sure I was ready anyway. I was just seven months.

When we got back home, granddaddy told us my sister had come by. He told her that we had gone to the hospital.

Momma and I went home. The next day I heard someone bamming on the door, and I thought I was still dreaming. I opened my eyes and still heard the noise. I looked around, and nobody was home but me.

"Here I come," I yelled.

Who's bamming on the door like the police? I got to the door looked out; it was Aunt Ester. I opened the door; she looked like she had seen a ghost.

"Aunt Ester, what's wrong?" I asked her. She grabbed me and hugged me.

"You're still pregnant?" she said.

"Uh, yes," I said.

"Oh my goodness," she said. "Thank you, Jesus."

"What's going on?" I asked.

I've been to every hospital in the city looking for you.

"Why?" I asked.

"Your sister told me you had the baby, and you died, and they had to bring you back to life."

"What?" I said.

"After that, I couldn't find you at the hospital. So, I went to your granddaddy's house, and he told me you were at home."

"She's damn crazy, I haven't seen her, and she didn't go to the hospital with me. So, I don't know why she's lying like that."

"I'm glad you're okay," she said, exhausted. "Call me when you have the baby," she said.

"Wait for me to call," I said, "don't listen to her." She hugged me and left.

Chapter

23

A few weeks later, my sister came home, and I didn't even bother asking her what she told Aunt Ester. She would only lie again. I knew she wouldn't be home long, especially with Walter staying here.

The house was almost done; granddaddy had someone working on it nonstop.

"Well, I think the house will be done just in time for you to have the baby," granddaddy said.

"That will be good," I said.

"Next week, I'll take you over there. The back room was one big room," he said, "so I split it for you and Walter to have a room. It's a little small, but it will do. Y'all will be able to get a bed and dresser in there."

"What about my sister?" I asked.

"Well, since she's older now, she can move down here with me," he said,

"She can stay in my back room where Bernice used to be. She should like it. She will have an outside entrance."

"Does she know that?" I asked.

"I told Martha to tell her," he said.

She may feel left out, I said to myself, but I didn't say anything.

***

I talked to Mark, "You're not coming to see me?" he asked.

"Why? Hell no!" I said, "Especially since I'm on bed rest. I'm big and hurting."

"Make sure you call me when you go into labor," he said.

"I will," I told him.

The following week, I told momma to take me to school. I had a paper that I had forgotten to turn in.

"Let me find us a ride," she said.

Lewis was down at granddaddy's house. She asked him to take us. They waited in the car while I went into the office. I was standing there waiting for my teacher when I felt something running down my legs. I went to the bathroom because it felt like I was peeing on myself. I sat on the toilet for a moment, but it didn't stop. I put some tissue in my panties then I went back to the office. My teacher was there, so I gave her my work, then I rushed back to the car.

"Momma," I said, swinging open the door. "I'm peeing on myself."

"No, you're not," she replied, "your water broke. I'm going to take you home and let you eat because they're not going to feed you."

We got home, and she cooked some breakfast for me. Then she told me to take a bath. Then, I put a towel between my legs because I was still draining. After that, she took me to the hospital. Once we got there, I called Mark. He said he was coming right up.

"I'll be back, Shawty," momma said.

"No," I replied, "don't leave me here by myself. I'm scared."

"Don't worry, Shawty, it's going to be hours before you have that baby. I'm just going down the street. I'll be right back."

I can't believe I'm in labor so early. I'm just eight months I wasn't due until June 4th.

About thirty minutes later, Mark came through the door eating McDonald's.

"No, you don't come in here with McDonald's, and I'm hungry."

He looked at his sandwich and said, "You want some?"

"Hell! No," I told him. "I mean, I do, but they said I can't eat."

"Oh, where has your momma gone?" he asked.

"She said she would be right back," I told him. "I'm glad you came. I've been calling granddaddy and looking for my sister."

"Hell! I don't remember the name, and she isn't anywhere to be found."

"Why isn't your granddaddy up here?" he asked.

"He doesn't believe in hospitals. The only way he will go to one is if he's dying. So no matter who's up here or what's going on, he will not go to a hospital. He won't drive, either. Years ago, he had a wreck that scared him so badly that he jumped out, left the car, and ran home. He has never driven since then."

"Dang! he said.

"Yeah, it's crazy, but he said he'd see us when we get home."

A little while later, Dr. Green came in. He and my doctor were partners.

"Where's my doctor?" I asked.

"Oh, he's on vacation. So I will be filling in for him," he said.

I made a face. I didn't like him; I wanted my doctor. I was comfortable with him. "Where's your mother?" he asked.

"She left," I told him.

"Well, when is she coming back?" he said, "You're dilating, and you're so young I don't want you in the room by yourself."

"I'm going in with her," Mark said, "I'm the father."

I don't know if he knew Mark was the baby's father or if he thought Mark was my father. The doctor made a face.

"We will wait a little while longer for her mother," he said. Then he left the room.

The contractions were coming back to back, and I couldn't take it, so I kept hitting the nurse button.

"Ms. Cook, we have given you all the medication you can have for the next four hours.

"If you don't come in here, I'm going to leave this hospital," I threatened. I was hurting so bad. Mark got up to try and hold my hand, and I bit him.

"Girl, what in the hell is wrong with you!" he said, yanking away.

"I'm hurting," I screamed, "and it's all your fault!"

Next, the nurse came into the room. "Let me set you up," she said. The minute she was close, I tried to bite her too. "Don't bite me," she yelled. "I'm trying to help you," she said.

"No, you're not!" I said. "I'm hurting."

After checking me, she said that I was far long enough for the epidural. Then, the anesthesiologist came into the room and explained all the risks.

"I was not listening, okay?" I said once he finished talking. "Just give me the medicine."

"Okay," he said, "be still; don't move if I stick the wrong place, I can paralyze you."

"What?" I said.

"Yes, he replied, "so be still."

Mark put his hand on my knees to hold me.

"Don't turn around," the nurse said.

So, of course, that made me want to look. Unfortunately, they were taking too long.

"Okay, here we go," he said.

I looked over my shoulder, and I saw this long needle. It was so long it looked like it would come through my chest. I screamed and tried to jump down, but he stuck the needle just in time. By the time I screamed, it had become numb. The next thing I know, I lay back relaxed in the hospital bed about to fall asleep.

Chapter

24

"Tosha, wake up," the doctor said, shaking me.

"I'm sleepy," I said.

"It's time for you to deliver. I need you awake so you can push," he said.

The medicine had me so drowsy I could barely open my eyes. I felt so good because I had been hurting so bad for hours. I got here at 11:00 a.m., and now, it was almost midnight.

"I was trying to wait for your momma," he said, "but your baby head is almost in between your legs, and you have dilated 12 center centimeters."

"Want me to go look for her?" Mark said.

"No," I said, grabbing his hand. "You can't leave me here alone."

"Well, I'll go after you go in recovery," he said.

"Roll her into the delivery room," the doctor told the nurse.

Once we were in there, I felt drunk. I had no complaints; I couldn't feel a thing.

"You can cut the umbilical cord," the doctor told Mark.

"I'm getting nervous," he said. "I've never been to the delivery room before."

Even though he had two kids already, two boys, I can't remember how old they were. I think they both were under five. They were probably between five and three at the time.

***

His baby mother's name was Veronica. I met her in school. Even though she was in the twelfth grade and I was in the ninth. One day, she walked up to me and introduced herself.

"Are you Tosha?" she asked.

"Yes," I replied.

"I'm Veronica, Mark's baby momma,' she said.

She was nice to me. She rubbed my stomach then asked what I was having.

She already had two sons by him. Even though she was older than I, she was fourteen, too, when she got pregnant with her first child.

***

The doctor said, "Tosha, if you don't push, I'm going to have to cut you some and get the suction to help pull her out." He threatened.

"Do it," I said. I was about to sleep. So he did.

Once she was out. Mark made a face.

"Oh goodness!" he said, shaking his head.

"What?" I asked.

"Man, your vagina opened up so big then closed back up. That was amazing."

The doctor gave him the scissors to cut the cord. Once he did, they weighed her, and she was four pounds and four ounces. I had an April fool's baby. She had yellow jaundice, so they took her to the incubator. Then they took me to recovery. I didn't remember anything else, just waking up. I woke up shivering; I was freezing.

"I'm cold," I told the nurse.

She gave me a heated blanket. After my time was up, they put me in a wheelchair to take me to my room. Once I got there, Mark was sleeping in my bed, and momma was on a couch.

"Dexter!" my momma yelled. She never got anyone's name right. "Get up; Tosha is here," she told him.

He responded to Dexter like that was his name. He got up so they could put me in my bed. The nurse left; they had a schedule to bring the baby in and out of the room.

"Momma, have you seen my sister?" I asked.

"No," she said.

"I don't know what I'm going to name the baby. I'll have to make up something."

"Name her after me," Mark said. *Now Mark, how can a girl's name be close to that? My name's Tosha;* I said, thinking to myself.

"I'm going to stop doing drugs," momma said, "I don't want the baby to go through what I put y'all through."

I cried. I sat there thinking of what to name my baby.

"Veronica," I said. That sounds good. It's a little like mine and a little like his, I guess. I'll just keep this name in case my sister doesn't show up.

I had a vaginal delivery, so I'd only be here for three days, and I knew I'd have to name her soon. Well, it was sooner than we thought. That morning they woke me up to sign the birth certificate. We got down to the office, and I gave them the name.

"Make her last name the same as mine," Mark told her.

"Okay, where's your ID?" the lady asked. "Dang, I left it at home!" he said.

"Well, you got to have it," she told him.

He left then and went home to get his ID. I went back up to my room. I saw my daughter, and they showed me how to feed her. When it came time for me to be released, I couldn't take her with me. She had to stay under the incubator for seven days. I was sad to leave her, but at least I could go home and try to prepare for her.

I came back to the hospital daily to see her until she was released. I cried every day I was pregnant, and she did too. Now, I've had her. I realized I had to stay alive to fight for her. I couldn't leave her alone. Now, I had a purpose again.

Once I got home, my sister showed up.

"Where's the baby?" she asked.

"She's in the hospital."

"Why?" she asked. After I explained everything to her she said, "Did you remember the name?"

"No," I told her. "That's why I've been looking for you. Even if I'd remembered, I definitely wouldn't have remembered how to spell it."

"Dang," she said, "I thought you would remember it."

"Have you seen the house?" I asked.

"Yes, momma took me over there. Y'all will be moving soon, and I'll be going down to granddaddy's house."

"How do you feel about that," I asked?

She shrugged her shoulders.

Once my daughter came home, it was almost time to move into the house. Granddaddy would come down every day to see my daughter, but he wouldn't touch her.

"Do you want to hold her?" I asked him.

"No," he replied, "she's too little." He would stand over her to talk to her then leave.

Mark was a drug dealer, and he was giving me money for my daughter but not enough, in my opinion. Momma didn't want him around. She just kept talking about how old he was.

A week later, my sister called crying, saying to come home it was an emergency. I went home; she was in the room crying her eyes out.

"What's wrong?" I asked.

She just stood there crying. Momma came flying through the door.

"Hey, what's the matter?" she asked.

"Aunt Ester called me and said my daddy is dead," she replied.

"What?" momma said, "Why she wouldn't call me? And why you're crying? You don't know him."

***

My momma and my dad were married for five years. When they split, my sister was around five, and I was three. I didn't remember him at all. I'd only seen him once.

I remember he came over with two coats: a pink one for me and a purple one for my sister. He brought my sister some flowers. I barely remember what he looked like since I only saw him that one time. But, I remember him being short with green eyes. Aunt Ester had one picture of him at her house from when he was younger in the military. He got discharged for some reason; I didn't know.

The day he brought the coats, he and momma left that night. That morning momma came back crying. She said her and my dad went to Arbor Place to buy some drugs. My dad got out of the car and approached the drug dealers, and got the drugs. He told them that my momma had the money in the car. He ran off, and the guys came to the car, asking my momma where the money was.

"What money?" she asked. "You got it," the guy told her.

"I don't have any money," she said.

The guy named Greg smacked her, and my momma ran home. My dad came back apologizing, and that's why he brought my sister the flowers. We never saw my dad anymore after that. Shortly after he went to jail for murder.

Chapter

25

Momma called Aunt Ester.

"Hey Ester, this is Martha; my daughter told me you said their dad died."

"Huh?" Aunt Ester said.

"You didn't tell her he died?" she asked.

"No," Aunt Ester replied, "I haven't even talked to her.

"I don't know why my daughter has started all this lying. It doesn't make any sense."

"I don't know, either," Aunt Ester said. "But she needs to stop," she replied.

Aunt Ester was my dad's sister. We only knew her and Aunt Jean. He had two other sisters, but we hadn't ever met them. He had one brother.

Momma hung up the phone.

"Girl, what's going on with you? Why you're making up these lies?"

My sister just stood there.

"It doesn't make any sense," momma told her.

She went crazy, I was thinking. We couldn't believe anything she said, and why was she trying to kill everyone off? She had no excuse for the lies she had been telling. She would just always stand there and look once she was caught.

The next few days were kind of peaceful. We had begun packing so we could move. Momma had done what she said. She's been off drugs and helping me with the baby. However, she was scared to hold her, too, because of her size.

"Start stewing her," my Aunt Liz told me.

"What's that?" I asked.

"Start putting a dab of baby food or cereal in her milk. It will make her fat, and she won't get as hungry fast."

"Oh really," I said. "It won't hurt her?"

"Just a dab," Liz said.

So I tried it, we would see what happens.

The next day I went down to granddaddy's house. He was standing in his green room in a daze. Granddaddy had a green room full of flowers; he loved flowers and growing vegetables. The greenroom had all windows so they could get sunlight.

"Granddaddy, what's wrong?" I asked.

"I thought I was doing the right thing by getting y'all that house," he said.

"Why do you think you're not now?" I asked.

"Your aunts are giving me a hard time. Jackie keeps hollering that I could've given it to her daughter. Hell, she's married! I wanted y'all to stay close to me and have somewhere to go with your momma being on drugs. Jackie has been fussing since I bought it."

"Tell her to hush; it's none of her business and not her money," I said. "Why can't you just leave us your house?"

"It's already in your aunt's name," he said.

Since my aunt had a degree, she felt like we weren't intelligent enough to communicate with her. So she only talked to a few of her sisters. I don't know why they bothered with her.

They said my aunt went to visit her one time, and she wouldn't say that she was her sister. I would've gone off.

I guess that goes to their theory that nobody was granddaddy's kids but Jackie and Grace. But how would they know? One day Granddaddy told me he had been upset with my aunt because she got ten thousand dollars of his money and didn't give it back.

"How did she get it?" I asked.

"When I was working as a cook, I was getting paid five hundred dollars a week. I sent it to her to put in the bank. She didn't give it back."

"Dang!" I said.

"So she shouldn't have anything to say, either. Whether they like it or not, the house for Martha," he said.

"Well, they will get over it," I told him.

I went back home later that day my cousin Lisa came by.

"Girl, I work with Mark's momma at Walgreens," she said.

"How do you know that's his momma?" I asked.

"I already knew her."

"Oh really," I said.

"Yes, I told her you had the baby; she didn't know anything about the baby."

"She didn't?" I asked.

"Nope," she said, "but she knows now. I told her everything she needed to know."

"Like what?" I asked her.

"Your name and address, and I told her your daughter has his last name because she keeps asking me. She said she knew that he didn't get that little girl pregnant. She is very upset. I told her new granddaughter's name is Veronica."

Oh goodness, I was thinking.

"Yeah, she said, she's gonna contact you."

Oh great, I said to myself. But I didn't have time to focus on that; I had to figure my life out and what to do with my baby. After she left, I was sort of relieved. I wasn't ready to deal with his family and stuff yet. A few weeks later, momma took me to the human service to start my benefits.

"What benefits are these?" I asked my momma.

"Well, they will give you insurance and childcare for your daughter and food stamps to buy food. And you can get WIC for her milk."

"Oh dang, that's a lot!" I said.

When the caseworker called us to the back, they began to ask a lot of questions about Mark. When I told him his age and birthday, the lady was stunned.

"You didn't put him in jail?" she asked my momma.

"No, I should've," momma replied. "He manipulated her," momma said, "I may go back and put his ass in jail."

"No!" I yelled. "We've already talked about this," I told her.

"I don't care," she replied. " She's right; his ass is too old."

"Well, you surely didn't call the police on Larry!" I yelled, then I got up and walked away. I knew he was too old, but if you don't lock someone up for holding me down, you surely shouldn't lock someone's up for manipulation.

It was a quiet ride back home. Momma didn't mention locking Mark up again after that.

Chapter

26

I had been helping momma move our stuff. She had decorated my room in pink, and Walter's room was blue. My sister was going down to granddaddy's house. For the last few days, my side had kind of been hurting. I was at the duplex cleaning out the rest of the stuff, and I heard a knock on the door. I went to the door, and it was a lady and a man.

"Are you Tosha?" she said when I opened the door.

"Yes," I answered.

"You have my grandbaby?" she asked.

"Are you Mark's momma?" I said.

"Yes, I am," she said, "and this is my husband, Charles."

"Yes, I did have my daughter a few months ago."

I invited them in, and then I went to the room to get my daughter. I brought her out, holding her in my hands; I showed her to his momma. They both stared at her.

"She looks like Mark," the younger son said.

"Surely does," Charles said.

"Do you know how old he was?" she said to me.

My anxiety started kicking in.

"Yes, I did," I said.

"Wait until I talk to him," she said. "He knows better than this. He already got two kids; he doesn't take care of them," she said.

"Calm down," her husband said.

"What?" She replied.

I just stood there. They gave me some gifts for the baby. Then she gave me her number. I showed her that we were moving across the street. My momma walked in, and they knew each other from high school. They knew my daddy, too, from school. After that, they left. I was relieved; I could tell she was really upset.

"Momma, my side has been hurting," I said. "I don't know why."

"How badly?" she asked.

"Bad," I told her.

"Go down granddaddy's house and see if he got any medicine."

When I got down there, I told granddaddy what happened.

"You probably had a setback," he said.

"What's that?" I asked.

"You probably started moving around too fast after you had the baby," he said.

"Oh, I've been hurting for like a week now," I said.

"You'd better go to the doctor," he said.

I went back home and told momma what he had said.

"If you're still hurting, I'll take you tomorrow," she said.

I tried to lie down, but I ached all night. I got up that morning.

"Momma, I'm hurting," I said.

I was bent over and could barely stand up.

Momma got out the bed and tried to straighten me up. I screamed.

"Don't do that!" I yelled. "I can't stand up."

"I'm going to take you to the emergency room," momma said.

We took my daughter to granddaddy for him to watch. She was a little bigger since I had been stewing her.

We got to the ER to find out that my insurance had changed since I had the baby, and they wouldn't see me. They referred me to a small facility of Mccallie Ave. We had never heard of it before. They didn't help me, either. They just checked me out. They didn't have the machine to do an x-ray or do labs.

I went home hurting so bad. Granddaddy gave me some pain medication. I didn't know what was wrong with me. I couldn't stand straight up. It's like I was stuck. The medicine did help a little, and granddaddy would get me up daily and help me move around.

"Don't let your bones lock up," he said. He helped exercise my legs and gave me muscles relaxers. The ten care insurance was crazy. They had sent a ten thousand dollar medical bill for when I had my daughter. Now they won't even cover me for the doctor. We were arguing with the insurance company daily. Until it was fixed, we had to rehabilitate me ourselves.

After a few months, I slowly started getting better. I didn't have long before school started again, and I needed to get a job. Next year, I'd be going to Bob Jones since we were forbidden to go back to Mt. Brook High. My sister said she would go to Bob Jones High with me.

TOSHA COOK

I finally started to get better, and Mark had come to get my daughter and me. We were taking her to get her ears pierced and take pictures today.

"What've you been up to," he said.

"Man, I was sick," I told him.

"For real, what's wrong?" he asked.

"I have no clue; it's like my back got stuck or something."

"Dang, so you still hurt?" he asked.

"Nah, I'm better now. Your momma came to my house," I told him. "She was very upset."

"Yes, she came up there hollering and screaming at me," he said. "I told her it wasn't mine."

"What!" I yelled.

"I just told her that because she was mad."

"Oh, hell no!" I said. "Call her and tell her the truth, or don't ever call me again!" I demanded.

"Man, I know it's mine," he said.

"I don't give a damn," I said. "You don't deny my child; you must be crazy. Call her right now or end this shit!"

"Okay, okay," he said. So he called, and I listened.

153

"Momma," he said, "Well, it's true about the baby," he told her.

"I knew you were lying," she said, "the baby looks just like your other kids. You ought to be ashamed of yourself." He had to listen to the speech, and then he told her he'd call her back.

"You're happy now?" he said.

I didn't want to hear all that, so I told him, "Don't play with me. You deny my child or me, and it's wrap."

After we got done at the mall, we went up to his grandmother's house. His aunt was up there and was a little weird. She made noises and faces and was on drugs, too.

"Stay away from Mark," she told me. "He's nothing but a baby maker. I know your momma," she said.

Then she made a face and went out the door.

"She's crazy," he said.

I think she and my momma knew each other from the streets or in jail. He took Veronica in there to see his grandmother.

"She looks like your son," his grandmother said. "Why did you get that young girl pregnant?"

"Aw, he said, "now, it's time to go." He took me back home. And Veronica and I went into the house. Before I got out of the car, I told him I needed a car. I was going to get a job, plus I'd have a ride to school.

"How much you need?" he asked.

"About five hundred dollars," I told him.

"I'll see what I can do," he replied.

When I got in the house, I told momma I needed a job.

"I can change your birth certificate," she said, "on the typewriter to make you sixteen; that way, you can work."

"Really?" I said.

"Yes," she told me.

Now that momma was off drugs, she had started back working. I was going to get a job to help take care of my daughter. So far, granddaddy was doing it.

Momma had signed me up for welfare, and they gave me a certificate for daycare. She would be going to Kids Art by Dodson. It was by the Techwood Projects. When I went to sign her up, I stopped to holler at Heather. I hadn't talked to her, and she hadn't seen the baby.

"Girl, what have you been up to?" she said.

" I'm about to get a job. Next year I'll be going to Bob Jones High."

"Really?" she said. "Next year, I'm going to Spain Park High."

"Your baby's too little," she added.

"Yeah, I know," I told her.

We talked for a while, then I went back home. Now I had to focus on getting this job.

Chapter

27

M omma found me a car off Main Street; it was a 1988 Mustang and a blue two-door. They wanted eight hundred dollars cash. I didn't have any money.

I had gotten my first job at Bo Jangles on Amincola Highway, but I hadn't started yet. Momma had been working pretty well. She was buying stuff for the house. She loved decorating and putting up wallpaper. She was good at it, too.

"I've got three hundred dollars for you Shawty, for the car," she told me. "I had been saving up."

"Thank you," I said to her. "I'll ask Mark for five hundred. Maybe he's got it by now, I said.

"You better not be going with that boy," she yelled.

"I'm not," I said, and then I went into my room.

I didn't like Walter living with us. I didn't know why, but I was extremely mean to him. Maybe I felt like momma had no room to try and save anyone. Then it seemed like he took my sister's place. His mother, Sherry, had come crying to my momma one night, telling her to keep him.

"I can't do anything for him," she said, slobbering. "Kathy messed me up."

Kathy had left her kids when they were toddlers, so they had to go from house to house then they all ended up on drugs just like her. It still affected Sherry. She said that's why she couldn't care for Walter. My momma was in the living room crying and talking with her. We didn't see her too much after that.

Walter had been getting into it at school with some guys. Momma had to keep going to the school to talk to the principal. He was going to Spain Park High also. One day, he came out of the room, complaining about something. I don't even remember what; I just snapped. Momma had cups on the wall for decorations. I grabbed one off the wall and was about to hit him with it.

"No!" my momma yelled.

"Tosha, don't do that; you could hurt him."

I didn't know why I always wanted to fight him. He was the only cousin I was around at the time. My other cousin didn't come around. They didn't want their kids around me. They didn't want them pregnant, thinking I would influence them. Not knowing I was trying to figure out how I even got pregnant.

I was on birth control since I had Veronica. The doctor gave me the Depo-Provera shot. I wasn't thinking about sex, but I took the shot, anyway, just in case. I wouldn't be having another baby, that's for sure.

I hadn't been as social because I was completely depressed. After work, I would just come home and go to my room. Momma noticed I was depressed but didn't say much. She would come to my room to make sure Veronica and I were okay. I stayed in there all day with the door closed.

"You don't want to go out with your friends?" she asked.

"No," I told her.

"I think you should go to meet friends and come out of this room," she said. "I'm worried about you," she added, "I think you would hurt Veronica or yourself."

She encouraged me to make some friends because I wouldn't talk on the phone or anything anymore. But, I didn't want to. I felt like my life was ruined, and I had to pick up the pieces. I was determined to graduate, if nothing else. School was about to start.

Mark had given me the money, so I got the car. I had been working, and that's how I was putting gas in it. The first week of school was kind of crazy. I had to adjust to taking my daughter to daycare. Plus, going to school and work, I had a full load.

Momma and granddaddy helped out a lot. After a few weeks in school, I made some friends, some I already knew, some I had just met. I met a new friend; her name was Olivia. She was nice, and she didn't live too far from my house. She lived by Notre Dame. She was light-skinned with green eyes and looked just like her mother; they looked like twins.

I took some elective classes, auto mechanics and Spanish. I needed to learn how to fix cars. Ours always broke down. My sister was barely coming to school. I got a feeling she was going to quit. That week Mark would be coming to see our daughter. All the visits now were mostly supervised. When momma was home, and we would be in the living room, he didn't stay long. I believe it was because we weren't having sex. We only had sex once since we had her, and she was almost six months old.

It was time for my check- up, and I went to see my OB doctor. "How're you doing, young lady?" he said.

"I'm okay," I told him.

"I see you lost all that weight soon as you dropped that baby."

"Yeah, I did," I told him.

"I've checked you for STDs; I'll call you with the results," he said.

"Okay," I told him.

Since I was down the street from Mark, I went there after the appointment. We were alone there, so we went to the back room. He had been to jail again, and his bag from Silverdale was on the floor. It had all the letters and the personal information they give you when released. We began to have sex. After we finished, he went into the bathroom.

I looked in his bag and saw some letters from some girls he had been writing while locked up. He came out of the bathroom, and I had the letters in my hand.

"What's this?" I said.

He just looked dumb.

"So you've been fooling around with other women."

"No," he said, "I don't care about them; I want you."

"Bullshit!" I said, "I read the letters you can have them."

He tried to grab my arm, and I yanked away and stormed out the door.

Chapter
28

I'm done with him, I told myself. It would be easy to cut him off because it wasn't like I had a physical connection with him anyway. It was more like sympathy sex. I felt like I owed him for helping me out. Without the situation, he wouldn't have been my type. He wasn't that attractive. Now Meco, that was another story. He was gorgeous, had smooth skin, and had nice hair. I used to see him all the time in the Techwood Projects, and I would just melt. I almost walked into a tree one time, staring at him. He would be my type.

One time Otis told me if I walked to the store for him. He would give me a picture of Meco. Him and Meco were best friends. So, of course, I went. I still had the picture, and I looked at it from time to time. He's so fine.

Anyways, I'm done with Mark, plus he barely helps me with our daughter, and all he wants to do is have sex, and I don't like it. Granddaddy had been buying all her clothes; I'm getting milk and stuff from WIC.

He was coming through, now and then, with twenty dollars here and there. It wasn't consistent.

The next day at school, I sat with Olivia. She and I had been getting close. She was like my closest friend at school. I was saving my money, I told her. "Girl, I bet you are," she said.

"I'm not going to be broken down in the hood with my daughter. I'm making it out of here."

"Girl, you will," she said.

She always encouraged me. Then I started telling her about Mark.

"He sounds like a mess," she said.

"Tell me about it," I replied.

A week later, I received a letter from the doctor saying I needed to come in to go over the test results. I called to schedule the appointment.

"Hey, lady," the doctor said as he walked in the door. "You got a little problem, but I'm going to fix you right up."

"What kind of problem?" I said.

"You tested positive for gonorrhea."

"What's that?" I asked.

"You just don't know anything to do you," he said. "It's a sexually transmitted disease."

"What!" I said.

"It's okay, lady. You're going to be alright."

"Bullshit!" I yelled.

"Now, don't go beating up on the man," The doctor said with a smile. "I'm going to give you a shot, and Charlotte is going to take you back to watch some videos so you can learn about STDS," he said.

I began to cry. I'm going to kill his ass when I leave here. She put me in a room, and I watched a video. She gave me all kinds of pamphlets to read. I had to learn about what was going on. He told me to come back in two weeks to be re-tested.

I left out of the parking lot on two wheels. I got to Mark's house and barely parked the car before jumping out.

"You got me fucked up!" I yelled.

"What's wrong with you," he said.

"Motherfucker, the doctor said I got gonorrhea. I took my purse off my shoulders and swung and hit him with it."

"Girl, stop hitting me." he said.

"You nasty bitch! I didn't want to have sex anyway. If you were going to sleep around, you could just do it and leave me alone." Then I took off my shoe and threw it.

"Girl, stop," he said, blocking my hits.

"You won't ever touch me again. You nasty bastard!" I got my stuff and left.

Now I was beginning to hate him. He talked me into sex, got me pregnant, didn't help me, and gave me disease, oh hell no!

The next few weeks went pretty peacefully. I went back to the doctor to get re-tested, and I was negative. I hadn't talked to Mark. My car had broken down. Then we had a terrible problem. The police had come by the house asking questions about the car. Come to find out, momma had paid for the car and didn't have the titles. The guy she bought it from told her he lost it, so she filed for lost title. It just so happened the car had been reported stolen.

The seller was a mechanic. He was fixing people's cars and selling them. So we had to give the car back. What a waste of money! Luckily, Bob Jones High had a bus stop right behind granddaddy's house. I'd have to catch the bus for now.

It was 6:30 AM. I was at the bus stop, and Mark and one of his friends pulled up.

"What do you want?" I said.

"Let me talk to you," he said.

I shot him a bird. He laughed, and gave me thirty dollars for our daughter, then pulled off. He was a piece of shit, thinking he was going to twenty and thirty dollar me to death. Plus, he hardly came to see her or anything since I wasn't fooling with him. And why in the hell, he up at 6.30 a.m. anyway? They had to have been geeked.

I told momma a few weeks later I had enough for a down payment on a car. I had six hundred dollars.

"Well, you can just buy this car around the corner from Rufus. He's got a brown pinto 1990," she said.

"What's that?" I asked.

"Come on, let's go around there, and I'll show it to you," she said.

Rufus was a mechanic that lived two streets over on Cleveland Avenue. His house was on the corner lot. He had so many cars in his yard, and he had a couple of tow trucks, too. He was black, fat, ugly, and dirty. He was always dirty every time we would come around there.

"Hey Martha," he said soon as we walked up, "is this your daughter?"

"Yes," momma said.

"Come on, let me show you the car," he said.

The car looked old, but it sounded like it ran well, and it was clean inside. I didn't care. I just needed a ride.

"What you think, Shawty?" momma said.

"I don't care," I said. "I just need a car."

"Okay, we will take it," momma told him.

"Make sure you get the title this time," I said to momma.

"I will," she replied.

This time we had the title and got the car registered. We'd see how long this lasts.

Chapter 29

I changed jobs. I got tired of Mark coming by my job. Even on days I wasn't there, he came. He didn't even want anything.

I started working at the Hardees by my school. The school year was almost over, and my grades were good. I got inducted into the Renaissance Society, which was like the honor society. They had dinner and gave me awards and a trophy. Momma came to the program with me. That's when I finally told her my sister had dropped out.

"What!" momma yelled. "Why you haven't been telling me?"

"I was waiting to see if she came back, but she never did."

The next day momma went over to my sister's friend's house, woke her up, and made her take the test to get her GED. She passed the test on the first try. She wasn't dumb; she just stopped going to school.

Working at Hardee's was about the same as Bo jangles, just a further drive. Mark had been very adamant about talking to me. He was like a Jack in the box. He would just pop up places that I was.

Olivia and I decided to go to a basketball game. She had a boyfriend named Logan, and Logan had a brother named Henry. They were both nice-looking men. They were light-skinned with good hair. We talked at the game, and when we left, I went to drop her off and saw Mark at the end of her driveway.

"Where's Veronica?" he said.

Veronica was at home. How the hell did he even know I was friends with Olivia? Then to know where she lived, he must damn well be following me.

"Why are you following me?" I asked.

"You must be crazy. I didn't follow you," he said.

"You're a damn liar," I said. "How else do you know where I was?"

Logan and Henry walked out of Olivia's house and got in the car.

"Oh, why are you in here with some niggas?" he said.

"Hey, I don't have to answer you. Get away from my car before I run your ass over."

He stood there, so of course, I hit the gas. He finally moved out the way so he wouldn't get hit. As soon as I got home, he was right behind me. I got out of the car.

"Tosha, let me talk to you," he said.

"Boy get the hell on," I told him.

He ran up on the porch. "I just want to talk," he said.

"What in the hell do you want?" I said.

We sat on the swing on the front porch.

"Were you talking to one of those guys?"

"Maybe," I said with a smirk on my face.

The next thing I knew, I heard a loud noise. It was almost like I passed out. Then, it was like a flash. I opened my eyes and saw him running out the gate to his car.

My momma came out on the porch saying, "What was that noise?"

"I don't know," I said.

"Why is he running?" momma said.

"I don't know. It seems like he did something to me. I heard something, but I didn't feel anything. I don't know if I passed out or what," I said.

"Wait, turn around," momma said. I turned my head to the side.

"He slapped you!" momma yelled.

"How you know?" I asked.

"His handprint is on your face," she said.

"What!"

I ran into the house and looked at my face. I had a big handprint on my face.

"I'm going to kill him," I said.

"I don't want you seeing him," momma said.

"I wasn't. Olivia and I were at the game. He must have followed me to her house."

"He's crazy. I'm calling the police on his ass," momma said. "He must have lost his mind."

I know, I was thinking, I hadn't told her about the pop-ups or the disease he gave me. He was trying to reassure me that he didn't want to cheat on me anymore. Instead, he was acting too possessive and crazy.

After momma threatened Mark with the police, I hadn't heard from him in a while. Walter's school troubles had started back. He had fought one guy who was threatening to bring his older brother. My sister and her friend had been waiting at the bus stop for him daily, making sure they didn't gang him.

One day my sister and her friend were late. By the time they got there, Walter had already been attacked. From what we heard, the brother was waiting and had a bat. He beat Walter in the head. By the time my sister came, the guy was in the Police car, and Walter was on the stretcher. My sister went crazy. She started pulling on the police car, trying to get the boy. The police made her leave.

Walter had emergency brain surgery that night. When my sister came home with blood all over her, it just broke my momma.

"I'm sorry, momma, I was late," she said, sobbing.

We all cried. The surgery didn't guarantee that he would live. So we had to just wait and see.

Chapter
30

Walter made it out of surgery and was in Intensive Care. It was so sad. Sherry had been coming by, and Momma had told her what happened. They had been going to the hospital together to see him.

On the first court date, they went to the hearing together. They put it off so they could get an attorney. The guy's momma was making excuses for him, saying Walter started the fight. He was just a juvenile, so they wouldn't try him as an adult, but momma wanted them to. Momma and Sherry were arguing with his family and the DA at the courthouse. It was a mess.

The court date was put off for a few months. A few weeks went by Walter finally came home. His head was so swollen that he sort of looked like the elephant man. It was wrapped in bandages. You could see blood on them, so it must be draining or something. He just lay in bed most of the day. He could barely move around.

Momma wasn't going to court anymore; Sherry told her she was going instead. So far, the case just kept getting put off. I was going to look for a job closer to home. It was a long drive to Hardees, and it's closer to the Bob Jones High school.

Mark still wasn't doing his part. He only wanted to know what I was doing. He came by the house to take me to Veronica's doctor's appointment. My car had broken down, and Rufus was supposed to fix it.

"Man, I miss you," he said.

I just sat there like he wasn't talking to me.

"I need another chance," he said.

"I wish I would," I said.

When we got close to the house, he pulled out a gun and sat it in his lap. He put the car in park.

He said, "we gone get back together, right?"

I was terrified.

"Yes, sure," I told him.

"Good," he said. He reached over and hugged me.

"Well, let me go; I have to go to school and work tomorrow." I grabbed Veronica and ran into the house.

I burst through the door "Momma!" I yelled.

"What!" she said, running out of her room.

"He pulled a gun out on me."

"What? I'm going to call the police on his ass. I told you not to deal with him," she yelled.

"I'm not," I said. "He took Veronica to the doctor."

Once the police came, we filed a report. I didn't know what to do he was crazy. Lord, I don't need this.

"You found a man just like your daddy," momma said.

Mark must seen the police at the house. The phone rang, and I answered.

"Why you called the police, bitch?" he said.

I just hung up. He was completely nuts. I didn't know what I was going to do. My sister had been around more had been giving me a ride some days.

I set it up where Mark would have to get Veronica from granddaddy's house. I didn't want any contact with him. It was my eleventh-grade year, and I was still at Bob Jones High. That year I'd be retaking auto mechanics. I needed to learn how to fix cars since mine kept tearing up.

Walter was now in a group home. After he healed from the surgery, it was like he just went crazy. He started hanging with the boys across the street. They were stealing cars. Breaking into people's houses, he kept getting caught. So they put him in a group home. I believe the boy that attacked Walter just got away. Sherry had stopped going to court, and Momma was so upset when she found out.

"If she would've told me," momma said, "I would've been going. Now they got away with what they have done."

Walter would have to stay in the group home until he was eighteen.

One day my sister took me up to Mark's house to get Veronica. He called my granddaddy, saying he wanted to see her. Then he wanted me to come to get her after having her for only two hours.

"He's so stupid."

"Yeah, he is," my sister said.

We pulled up at Mark's house, and he was sitting on the porch. Our daughter was standing next to him.

I got out of the car, "Veronica, come on," I said.

"Don't go over there," he told her.

"Why did you tell her that?" I said. "You told me to come to get her."

"Let me talk to you," he said.

"I don't have anything to say; give me my baby." He got up and started towards me.

"Don't come near me," I said.

Veronica was just standing there looking.

"Veronica, come on," I said, clapping my hands at her, but she didn't move.

I started towards her, and he grabbed my arm.

"Let her go," my sister said, getting out of the car. She ran over with a can of mace and sprayed him.

"Come on," she said, grabbing my arm. The mace didn't work on him. He was still chasing us. "You had a baby by Michael Myers," she said, jumping in the car.

I got to the car and couldn't get the car door open.

"Come on!" she yelled.

"The damn door won't open!" I yelled.

He was getting too close; I jumped through the window. My sister grabbed me by the hand and held on to me as we pulled off. My body wasn't through the window. When we got to the bottom of the hill, she stopped the car to let me in. We got home and told momma what happened. She turned around and went right back up there.

Mark was still on the porch in the same spot with mace running down his face. Veronica was still standing there looking. He didn't even wipe his face off.

"What the hell have you gotten yourself into?" my sister said.

"I don't know," I replied.

As soon as momma got out of the car, he started explaining.

"Your ass needs to be in jail anyway," momma said.

"No, Mrs. Martha, they're trying to gang me and mace me," he said.

"He's lying!" I yelled. "He wouldn't give me Veronica and kept trying to fight me."

"Give me this baby," momma said.

She went to the porch got Veronica. He was following behind her, trying to play the victim. Momma didn't even answer him; she just kept walking. We got in the car and left.

Chapter

31

I got a job at Wendy's by my school. It was still out east, but it was a lot closer than Hardee's. Besides, I didn't want Mark to know where I was; he had turned into a straight stalker. When Mark popped up at Hardee's, I knew it was time to go.

Wendy's was kind of fun, and the manager was super cool; her name was Tracy, and she was white but married to a black guy and had mixed kids. I put my daughter in a daycare around the corner on Gagg Road. She was good at home but had been extremely troubled at daycare. I wasn't sure why.

I was at work one day when the daycare called. "Ms. Cook, yes, this is Sharon at the daycare; you need to come to get Veronica. She had hit a little girl in her eye."

"Really?" I said. I hung up the phone in disbelief. "Tracy, I have to go get Veronica," I told her.

"Again?" she said.

"Yes again. I don't know what's going on with her."

I went to the daycare all her ponytails were pulled out of her head.

"What happened to her hair?" I asked.

"She pulled it out."

"What?"

The lady told me that Veronica just threw a fit, threw chairs, pulled her hair, and hit the little girl. I believed they were lying on my baby.

"Veronica," I said. She ran to me smiling.

There is no way she did all this; she was only two years old. So, we had a meeting, and they told me if Veronica's behavior continued, she would have to leave the daycare. I left the daycare. *These white folks are racist*, I said to myself. I took her to granddaddy so I could go back to work.

"Granddaddy, can Veronica stay? The daycare called, saying she was acting badly. I don't believe them," I said.

"Oh, yeah, that girl's got a problem," Granddaddy said.

"Why do you say that?" I asked.

"Hell, she acts crazy all the time!" granddaddy replied.

"It's funny she doesn't do it with me," I told him.

"Well, I'm telling you something is wrong with her; she needs help."

"No, she doesn't," I said. I was holding Veronica, and she was just smiling at me. "They better leave her alone," I said as I was leaving.

***

They liked me a lot at Wendy's. They gave me an award for being the most dependable. Tracy told me they would promote me to shift leader if I stayed.

The weekend came, and my sister asked me if I wanted to go to a basketball game. Momma was so happy I was getting out of the house. She would watch Veronica with no problem. I still suffered from depression, but this helped.

We went to the game, and we saw some old friends. We had gone to Easton Middle with Luke and Lance. My sister wanted to go over to Luke's house because they were having an after-party after the game. He stayed right by Bob Jones High School. It was crowded over there. Some people we knew, some we didn't. Luke had a girlfriend named Shelia; she seemed nice and was older than us. She was going to school at TSU. I had never seen her before, but her cousin Melody was with her, and she used to be my childhood friend.

"Hey Melody," I said, "girl, what you been up to?"

"Nothing, just hanging out with my cousin. Do you know her?" she asked.

"No, I don't," I said.

She took me over to her car and introduced us.

"Hey," Shelia said.

"Hey, my name is Tosha, and this is my sister."

We talked, then we exchanged numbers. Maybe they will be some new friends to hang out with. I didn't talk to Heather much since I no longer went to the Techwood Projects.

After we left there, I called Shelia the next day. That's when I found out she lived right up the street from me. She stayed in her grandmother's house. It was a really nice, huge brick house with two stories.

She had two main friends that she hung out with, Sherry and Mary. I went over there, and she introduced us. They were so much bigger than I was; they made me look like a little shrimp. They partied all the time every weekend.

I had to get another car because Rufus whooped us on that car. He never fixed it, and I got tired of going around there arguing with him. So I went on Rossville Boulevard and got a black Nissan puzzler.

A few weeks went by, and I was at home lying in bed at about 3 AM. I heard a knock on my window, so I lifted the blinds to see who it was and it was Mark. He had blood running all down his face.

"What are you doing, and what happened to you?" I said.

"Man, come help me. We got into a fight, and I got stabbed," he said.

"Why are you here? Why didn't you go to the hospital?"

"Come to the door, please," he said.

I went out the front door momma was asleep.

"What do you want," I said.

"Come and go to the hospital with me," he said.

I went to the car, and there were two of his friends in there. They were all beaten up.

"What happened?" I asked.

Henry in the back started telling me a play-by-play of what happened. So, George, the other guy who was driving, said, "Man, how do you know? Were you even helping us?"

"Man, yes," he said, "don't play me like that."

We finally pulled up at Erlanger hospital.

Chapter

32

We arrived at the hospital, and they put Mark straight in a room. The nurse came in ran some tests, then they started asking questions about what happened. Mark kept telling them he didn't remember much. The more questions they asked seemed to make him more nervous. When the nurse was about to leave out of the room, he said he was going to the bathroom and went out.

Thirty minutes had passed, and a guy came in the room and asked me, "Are you Tosha?"

"Yeah, why?"

"Mark told me to come and get you."

"What?" I said.

TOSHA COOK

"Yeah, he's down the street," he said.

He's down the street? The guy walked me down the street to a green house, the second house from the corner. I went in straight cursing.

"Why the hell did you leave me up there like that?"

"I had warrants," he said. "The police were coming, so I had to leave."

"You could've left me at home," I said.

He just wanted to come to get me for sympathy. The lady's house we were at Mark kept referring to her as the nurse. She was pouring something on him; I think it was peroxide, and then she bandaged him up. Fooling with him, no telling who she was. After she bandaged him, we left, and he took me back home. We pulled up to my house.

"Don't be popping up here in the middle of the night scaring me like that anymore," I told him.

"I'm sorry I was just scared and wanted you to come with me," he said.

"Boy, you were not scared, I told him. "With all the shit you are involved in."

"I'll call you tomorrow," he said.

187

I got out of the car and closed the door. The next few days went by, and I decided to call Heather. I hadn't talked to her in a while since I met some new friends.

"Hey girl," I said, "how's it been going?"

"Nothing, what you been doing?"

"Nothing, just working and going to school."

"Girl, I been meaning to call you," she said. "Mark has been fooling with Ashley. I go to school with her, and she told me,"

"Really?" I said. I was about to curse him out.

"She said they have been messing around for a while."

"Okay, I'm about to call him. I'll call you back," I told her.

I hung up and immediately called Mark.

"Nigga this is what I'm talking about. You're supposed to be messing with Ashley. Heather just told me you did."

"She's a damn lie," he said.

"No, you're the liar. Why you just don't talk to them hoes and leave me alone?" I hung up the phone.

The next few days, he called and called. I didn't answer; of course, he showed up at my door.

'Boy, what you want."

"Man, I promise, Tosha, she's lying," he said.

"I don't believe you," I told him.

"Okay, call her right now. I can prove it."

Well, coincidence, I didn't have to. She called; when I picked up, Mark told me not to say he was there.

'Hey girl, what's up?"

"Nothing, what are you doing?" she said.

"Just in here with Veronica."

"Have you talked to Mark?" she asked.

"No," I said.

"He has just left Ashley's house."

"When?"I asked.

"Just a few minutes ago," she told me.

"Today?" I asked.

"Yes, today. I came right home to tell you," she said. "hmm, well, I'm not with him anymore anyway," I told her, then I made an excuse to get off the phone.

When I hung up, Mark said, "I told you the bitch was lying."

I was hurt; why would she lie to me? Mark had been at my house for a while so she couldn't just seen him. I was confused. I thought she was my friend.

A week later, I went to the Techwood Projects to see Neka. Neka was one of the friends I kept in contact with. I used to keep her kids while they went out. I was letting her see my daughter.

When I left, I rode past Heather's house. She and a few more of her friends were on the porch.

"Bitch!" they yelled as I rode by.

She had been calling, and after she lied, I wouldn't answer her anymore. I guess she was mad. I went to Neka's house two more times. Each time I rode by, they would holler out 'bitch'.

Well, one day, I didn't feel like being a bitch. So I went around the corner to where my sister was staying.

"Hey, come back around Heather's house with me."

"Why, what's going on?" she asked.

"She keeps calling me bitch, and I don't feel like being a bitch today."

"Okay," she said, "let me get this bat."

She went into the house and got an iron baseball bat, and then she got in the car.

Chapter

33

I pulled up in front of Heather's house and rolled the window down.

'Who do you keep calling a bitch?" I asked her.

There were three of them, and I could hear them talking shit from the porch. Heather was a big girl, probably 5'7" and 180 pounds. I was extremely small. I was 4'10" and 98 pounds. I always remembered my momma saying I had dorfy hands and that I needed to pick up something to hit them with. Today I didn't have anything to pick up.

Heather started walking towards my car. When she got close enough, I swung the car door open. When I did, she stumbled back, so I jumped out of the car and started hitting her, then we both fell to the ground. I was on top of her, and they all dived on me. My sister got out of the car with the bat and started hitting all of them. One by one, as she hit them, they ran. She even hit me trying to hit Heather.

Her parents came outside and started breaking it up. A guy from across the street came and took the bat from my sister.

"She's going to hurt somebody," he said. "I was watching from across the street, and she was swinging the hell out of that bat."

Heather's momma said, "Tosha, please go home."

"She started with me!" I screamed.

I looked and saw my daughter in the back seat. I started to feel bad; I needed to take her home, so we left.

"Are you okay," my sister asked.

"My back hurts," I said, "You hit me with the bat."

"I didn't mean to," she said.

"Yeah, I know."

I went home, and momma wasn't there. I looked at my hair, and it was pulled all up. My cousin Tonya had put finger waves in my hair, and those girls had pulled them all out. I had a bruise on my back from my sister hitting me with the bat and some scratches on my face.

Momma came in, and I ran up front.

"Momma I said, "Heather ganged me."

"What?" she said, "Why?"

"They kept calling me a bitch, and I stopped. We got into a fight. My sister was with me, and she hit me with a bat."

"What!" momma screamed.

"She didn't mean to; she was trying to hit Heather."

"Come on," momma said, "let's go up there."

Of course, we stopped and got Kathy. We arrived at Heather's house. Kathy got right out of the car, pulled out a knife, and walked into their house like she lived there.

"Who ganged my motherfucker niece?" she said.

Heather had a scarf wrapped around her head. She said that my sister burst her head while hitting her with the bat. It must not be that bad because she wasn't at the hospital.

Heather told her side of the story. She said she didn't start it; I did. I said she started it.

Her momma said, "Tosha, get Kathy out of my house."

I saw we wouldn't get anywhere, so I told them to come on, and we left. I never saw Heather anymore after that.

A few weeks passed, and I was at work until the daycare called again. I went up there for a meeting. Veronica had been still fighting and acting out. So they made me take her out. I didn't want to tell granddaddy because I didn't want to hear the comments that she needed help. That would make me mad, so I put her in daycare on the same side of the town. It was called Childcare Network. The good thing was that it was a 24-hour daycare also.

Shelia and I had been hanging out. Momma was so glad that I was being social, so she didn't mind me going out. She didn't want me in that room being depressed. Today was college night at the Whole Note.

Shelia said, "Hey, you want to go?"

"Well, I'm not old enough. How would I get in?"

"We will pass the ID to the back," she told me.

"What does that mean?" I asked.

"After I use my ID, I'll put it in my left hand and pass it back so you can use it."

"Okay," I said, "if you think that will work."

"Now, we got to get you some clothes," she said.

"What's wrong with what I'm wearing?" I said.

She turned around and looked at me and said, "Oh no! You need something to show your shape. You got big butt and hips."

"I do," I said.

"Yes," she said, "you can't see it because you're hiding it."

We went to the mall, and she picked out an outfit for me. The pants were boot cut with a shirt.

"Dang! she said, "your butt is huge."

"Stop!" I said I don't like drawing attention to myself.

"Damn lie," she said. "You're surely going to get attention with this ass. Girl, why have you been hiding it?"

We both laughed. We went out that night, and it was fun. I don't dance, so I mainly just sat around watching; but Shelia and her crew scrubbed the ground all night. I was in shock that the ID trick worked. When we left the club, momma was up waiting.

"How was it Shawty?"

"It was fun," I told her.

"That's good," she said, "I'm glad you're getting out the house. It's 2 AM, but you're still going to school."

"Momma," I said.

"Nope," she replied, "you have to go to school.

I'm going to be tired, but I believed it was worth it.

Chapter

34

That weekend, Shelia asked if I wanted to go to a party downtown at a hotel. I told her yes. I was feeling better about myself, still sad every day, but at least this would take my mind off things for a while.

Shelia picked me up with her boyfriend Luke driving; I was in the back seat. We pulled up at the Texaco gas station and parked. People would just go there to hang out, and it was so crowded. People were everywhere, both inside and outside the gas station. People were sitting in cars.

The next thing I knew, Mark was pulling up on the side of us with two of his friends. Aw, hell! He came up to the car and started knocking on the window.

"Boy, get away from this car," I said.

"Open up the door," he said.

I sat there and ignored him, so he went to the driver's side of the car and started threatening Luke.

"Man, I'm not with her; I'm with Shelia," Luke explained.

"Man, damn him," I said. "Let's go to the party," I told Shelia, so we pulled off and went to the hotel party.

They had a few rooms they were partying in and out of, so we went from room to room. Of course, I looked up, and there was Mark. I grabbed Shelia by the arm.

"Come on, I told her."

"I'm scared," she said.

"We can't show fear," I told her.

I pulled her arm, and we went out of the room. We went down the escalator to get out of the hotel. Mark was right on the side of our car, ranting and raving. I kept talking to Shelia like he wasn't right there.

"I can't do this," Shelia said.

"Oh, you, Ms. Foxy brown, now," he said.

I had worn a brown coat. I still acted like he wasn't right there. We walked outside; he hocked and spit. I stopped and looked at my clothes Because if any spit got on me, I would kill

197

him. He's lucky it didn't get on me because I was going to go crazy. Finally, we made it to the car, and we pulled off.

"He is damn crazy," Shelia said.

"Yeah, I know. That's why I'm not fooling with him. He only wants to know where I am and what I'm doing. He didn't even ask about our daughter."

We were almost at her house, sitting at the red light. Next thing you know, somebody came up to the car and started knocking on the window. It scared the shit out of us. She hit the gas and ran the light. I turned around and looked back; it was Mark. Oh goodness, he is Michael Myers.

"Damn girl, what you do to him," Shelia said.

"Nothing," I replied. "He is crazy."

"He scares me," she said. "What, is he damn following us?" she said.

"I guess so; he just popped up out of nowhere."

***

All the partying made me tired. So now, I was back to work. The year was about to over, and I was enjoying auto mechanics. I took Shelia's truck in because it needed breaks. The teacher would let us bring in family cars for simple repairs, and we fixed her breaks and rotated the tires. When I left school, I had to get my daughter from daycare. She was still fighting and tearing up her hair.

"I went to get her," the teacher said. "She looks so pretty when you drop her off. Then she just tears herself up."

"I don't know why she's doing that."

I find it so hard to believe. She looks so innocent when I pick her up. But I guess both daycares can't be lying. This time I went to my Aunt Ester; she had a daycare at friendship community church. I told her what had been happening, so she agreed to help me. Of course, it wasn't long before she called me.

"Tosha, I've done everything I could do, but this girl needs help," she said.

"Why does everyone keep saying that? She's just a toddler. She doesn't need any help." I fired back.

"Yes, she does," Aunt Ester said.

She sounded like granddaddy. I picked my daughter up, and she would just smile and hug me. There wasn't anything wrong with my baby. I took her and left. Now, this is about to be her fourth daycare.

The summer was here, and Shelia had another boyfriend. His name was Jamel; he ran with a group of guys. They called themselves The Squad.

One of them looked good and was built; his name was Greg. Matt was nice, and had a nice family. His momma was friendly and would cook for us a lot. There were times I would go and see if Matt was home. If he wasn't, his momma would invite me in and offer me food.

I needed Matt or Jamel to get me close to Chris. When Shelia would go to Jamel's house, I would say. Did you ask about Chris? Does he have a girlfriend or what? She finally called and gave me Chris' number.

I called, and we talked for a while, then he invited me over. We were sitting on the couch when I heard a noise. I looked out the window, of course, it was Mark! What has he got a tracking device in my ass or something! How did he find me? He went by my car, and I couldn't tell what he was doing, so I ran out there, and he pulled off. His ass is crazy, oh my goodness! I looked around the car, and I didn't see any damage. I was so embarrassed that I told Chris I would talk to him another time and left.

Chapter

35

ince Shelia introduced me to Matt, I'd been going up to his house. He was friendly, and so was his family. One day I went up to his house to see him, but he wasn't home, so his momma let me in. His momma was so nurturing. She was very touchy-feely. Matt was grown, and she would put him in her lap if he wanted her to. She was hugging and kissing me, too. Something about her that was so loving made me emotional. I would just cry all the time.

"What's wrong, baby?" she asked. I didn't know. We always knew momma loved us, but she wasn't hugging and kissing, and his mother was. She sat on the couch with me and rocked me as I cried.

One day, I just went ahead and told her I was molested. After that day, she became a second mom to me. I became extremely close with Matt and his family. They were like my adopted family now; Matt didn't even have to be there. I would hang with the rest of the family without him.

One day, Veronica and I were over there. Matt came home, and Veronica ran to him and said, "Daddy." *Uh no*, Matt and I were thinking,

"He's not your daddy."

"No," his momma said, "don't hurt her feelings. We will explain to her when she gets older."

"Well, okay," we said.

Mark wasn't coming around anymore since I wouldn't be with him. All he knew how to say when we talked was 'let me talk to you.' I thought, *Boy, we don't have anything to talk about.*

He acted like he wanted to see Veronica, so I took her to granddaddy's house, but he left once he saw I wasn't coming. He didn't ask for her again.

Now I'm a full-fledged part of Matt's family, and I would go there just about every day. His Momma was a great cook, and she was teaching me how to cook stuff. I'd never had so many hugs and kisses in my life. And she was soft; I started calling her momma, too.

"Momma, you're just like a pillow," I told her.

"I know," she said, laughing.

It was my twelfth-grade year, and my self-confidence was back to 100%. Shelia had given me a complete makeover. She was taking me shopping to buy cute clothes. She also would take me to different people to get our hair done. I had no clue since I didn't keep up with style much. She would also talk to me about sex; she was like my new big sister. She was the only child and was spoiled. I changed schools this year and started going to Eastland High School, just so I could hang out late and wouldn't be as tired.

School didn't start until 9 AM, and we were hanging out all the time. We would all pile up in Shelia's jeep with Shelia's girlfriends and Matt's guy friends. We would be like eight or nine deep. Matt's momma would keep my daughter, and we would party and just stay over there when we came back home.

Things were going well until I got another call. Veronica had got put out of daycare again. This time I had no choice but to tell granddaddy because all the daycares that accepted my voucher had a waiting list. Momma got back on drugs, and Veronica and

I had moved to granddaddy's house in the back room my sister was in. My sister had left and moved in with a friend.

"Granddaddy, can you watch Veronica? I'm working on getting her into another daycare."

"I told you she needs some help," he said.

"Yes, granddaddy, you told me, I know."

Now that momma was back on drugs, I clung even more to Matt's momma now. Now, I have to save money to get Veronica and me somewhere to live. This wasn't the life I wanted for us. I had been working well. It would be the first year that I'd be able to file taxes for myself. I had a plan to save my income tax money to save up for us a place.

I had a new job at BI-LO on Highway 58. When I got paid, I bought household stuff like bleach, toilet paper, paper towels, etc., and put it underneath my bed.

I had found a new boyfriend at school named Jamison. He was cute and had pretty eyes. I had mixed emotions about him, though. It seemed that some days I liked him and some days I didn't. One thing I hated was he smoked cigarettes, and I hated cigarette smoke.

A few months went by, and I got a call from my Aunt Ester.

"Hey, Aunt Ester," I said.

"Tosha, how're you doing?" she said.

"I'm okay."

"Well, I wanted to talk to you," she said. "I went to a teacher conference, and some of the ladies were there. I didn't know, but I heard them talk about Veronica and how bad she was and that they were going to put her out of the daycare. I didn't tell them you were my niece, but I just listened to them talk."

"Well, they had already put her out," I told her.

"I hate that," she said. "Where's she going now?"

"Nowhere," I told her. "Granddaddy has been keeping her."

"Well, I'll try to help you again," she said. "You can bring her back to my daycare," she suggested.

"Oh really?" I said, "Oh, thank you, Aunt Ester."

Lord, I just prayed that she might make it until she goes to regular school.

Chapter

36

This High School was different, but it didn't make a difference to me. I had some friends, but it didn't matter. My friends were outside of school. My grades were still good. I met a few friends, but most people wanted a ride home from school. One of my friends named Ellis would ask me to take him home and would tell me he had gas money.

"Pull up at the gas pump," he said.

I pulled up, and he got out and went to the pump. After he stopped pumping, my car was full. He got back in the front seat.

"Dang, I didn't know you were going to fill it up!" I said.

"You better pull off," he replied.

"What do you mean?"

"I haven't got money," he told me. "Hurry up before them people come to the store."

"You must be crazier than hell," I told him.

"Girl, hurry up," he said, "I don't have any money." I looked and could tell he was serious. I hit the gas and pulled off.

"You better not ask for any more rides," I told him. He laughed and went in the house.

Today I came home and guessed who popped up? Mark. I went outside, "Boy what do you want? Oh, let me guess, let you talk to me."

"I got something I want to show you," he said.

"What?" I replied.

"Come, look," he said.

I thought about it for a minute, and then I went over there. He held out his arm, and I looked closely, 'Tosha.' He had gone and got a tattoo with my name on his arm.

"What the hell did you do that for? That's stupid," I told him. "We're not even together, and what about your damn child!"

I guess this wasn't the reaction he expected. He got upset. He moved towards me, and I tried to run, and he grabbed me and slung me to the ground. I screamed, and granddaddy came out the door with a gun in his hand.

"Hey, old nigga!" granddaddy yelled. "You better let her go before I kill you,"

Mark struck out running. A few days later, he called. I just picked up the phone and held it.

"I think I'm going to leave town before one of us gets hurt."

"Well, I think that's a good idea," I told him. He moved to Georgia, and we didn't see him anymore after that.

I filed my taxes, and the money I got back, I put in my savings account. It was three thousand dollars. I'd save it until I turned eighteen and move out. I was going to graduate at seventeen since my birthday, isn't until September.

After a few weeks, granddaddy came into my room.

"Hey granddaddy,"

"Hey," he said. "Have you got your taxes back yet?"

" Yes, I did. I'm saving it for when I move," I told him proudly.

"Well, what are you going to give your granddaddy?" he asked.

"What do you mean?" I asked.

"Well, you're sitting on money," he said. "Aren't you gonna give me something?"

"Granddaddy, I'm not sitting on money. I don't have anything. We're going to be moving with the clothes on our backs," I said. "Just give me a few more months, and I'll be out of here," I said.

It was the turning point for us because Granddaddy became angry. My 12th-grade year became a nightmare. At granddaddy's house, I had a lock on my door. I was selling candy for a school fundraiser and had almost sold all the candy bars.

One day, I came home, and my door was unlocked. I went into my room and saw the candy, but the money envelope was empty.

"Hey!" I yelled. I ran up front where granddaddy was. "Who has been in my room?"

"I don't know," he said. Somebody went into my room and stole my candy money.

"Your momma came down here," he said. "She said she needed something in there, so I let her in," he replied.

"Why in the world would you do that knowing she is on drugs? That's lowdown."

I went into my room and cried. I couldn't catch a break. Veronica just came to me and laid on me.

"It's okay," I told her. "I'm going to get us out of here, you watch."

I fell back into a deep depression. I had to get us out of here; I had to be focused. I was lying in bed, and granddaddy came and put a letter on my bed. I opened it up and read it. It was from my Aunt; she was telling me that granddaddy's house was in her name and to get out. I was causing her dad stress.

Uh, you're causing him stress as well stealing his money. So, I politely wrote her back and cursed her out.

The next day, granddaddy came in the room arguing with me that I didn't wash the tub out.

"Granddaddy, okay," I said.

After he left, I went and washed it out. Later that day, my Aunt came bursting into my room.

"Tosha, you need to go wash that tub out like my daddy told you, too," she said.

"You better get out of my room," I said.

"My daddy said you're getting on his nerves and won't wash the tub out."

"I don't care what your daddy said and close my door, and I'm about to call and tell my momma."

What the hell is wrong with them! She talks about us like a dog, then tries and comes to tell me something. I'm not a kid anymore. She better go. I called my momma, and she and my Aunt got into it.

"Granddaddy, you're starting a lot of trouble," I said. "Now, how stupid do y'all look? Because the tub is already cleaned out."

These next few months need to go on by, oh my goodness!

Chapter 37

It was almost time for prom, and I was going with Jamison. My sister was going to let me wear her old prom dress. On the day of the prom, my sister and my Aunt Liz came to get me ready. Momma didn't come, but I was hoping she would.

My sister did my hair, and Aunt Liz did my makeup. I looked nice. I was about to be graduate. I couldn't believe I'd made it this far. I was going to go to college at Chattanooga state because I couldn't leave Veronica, so my dreams of being Matlock were out.

On graduation day, I felt so lonely inside. I had to get dressed alone. I could've gone up to Matt's house, but I stayed home thinking my momma would come. She didn't, but hopefully, she would be at my graduation. I sat on my bed about to put on my cap and gown. I should've been happy, but I felt so empty inside. Tears rolled down my face. I got dressed and left for graduation. Some of my momma's family were there, and I was surprised. Of course, Matt and his momma were there. Aunt Ester and my sister were downstairs when I came down off the stage. We took a picture on the steps; then I went outside to see and greet everyone. My momma had made it, so I was happy.

"I made it, Shawty," she said.

Matt and his momma walked up to me and asked what I was going to do afterward.

"I don't know," I said. "You know I won't be with my momma's family long."

"Okay," she said, "Come to the house. I'm going to cook something."

"Okay," I said.

My momma's family wanted to go to Ryan's.

"I guess so," I said.

We talked and ate after a while, and then I went up to Matt's house. He had a strange look on his face.

"What's wrong?" I said.

"Everybody left," he said.

"What do you mean?" I asked.

"We had a surprise party for you; when you didn't come, they left."

"What?" I said. "Why you didn't tell me?"

"Well, you didn't get along with your family, and we didn't think you would take this long."

"Y'all should've called me or something to get me over here."

"Momma had cooked all that food," he said.

"Oh, God! Now I feel bad." I went to momma's room. "Momma, I'm so sorry y'all should've called or done something to lure me up here or something."

"It's okay, baby," she said.

I went into the kitchen and saw all that food. I felt so bad. I was full, but I ate anyway because I felt bad. I took some food home, too.

Now that school was out, I got another job at Krispy Kreme. I'd be working part-time and going to school during the day. One of Matt's cousins worked there. She had been there for a few years. I got my sister to work there, too.

I was counting down to get out of granddaddy's house. I was just waiting for my birthday to come. When I turned eighteen, I

214

could apply for housing. Unfortunately, I had no idea where to start.

I came home one day to my door being open again. I went into my room; my starter jacket and some of my jewelry were gone.

"Granddaddy!" I screamed, "Why the hell do you keep letting her in my room!"

"Aw, shit!" he said.

"Aw, shit, nothing! Now my coat and jewelry were gone. I'm tired of this shit," I said.

I was furious. I was ranting, raving, and going off. He called the police and told them I tried to stab him.

"You're a damn liar," I said.

"Go and take her out of here," he said.

"Can I call my sister, please?" I asked the police.

My sister was at work, and when she came to the phone, I said, "Hey, come home, now I'm about to go to jail. Granddaddy has called the police on me. Come and get Veronica now!"

I asked the police if I could wait for my sister, he agreed. Then, low and behold, here she comes. She pulled up and jumped out of the car.

"Don't take my sister to jail, motherfuckers! She's just a child."

"Ma'am, you need to calm down," the police told her.

"Granddaddy, you know she didn't try to stab you with your low-down ass," she yelled.

I told her not to get in trouble.

"I need you to get my daughter." I was crying uncontrollably.

"Give me her," she said. She went and snatched Veronica right out of granddaddy's hand.

"I got to go to juvenile?" I asked the officer.

"Yes," he said.

I was out of tears; I couldn't even cry anymore. I turned to my sister to tell her to answer the phone when I called.

They put me in the police car, and I was completely traumatized. I was going to jail for something I didn't do. When I got to juvenile, they made me wash my hair.

"This is for lice," the lady said.

"Lice?" I asked.

"Yes, lice."

"I don't have lice," I told her.

"Doesn't matter; you've got to wash your hair with it anyway," she said.

After that, they put me in an orange jumpsuit and then locked me in the cell. The next morning I asked to use the phone. I called my sister.

"How is Veronica? She's okay?"

"Yes, she is," she said. "Are you okay?"

"Hell no!" I said. "When do I go to court?"

"In the morning," she said.

"Are you coming?" I asked.

"Hell, yeah!" she said.

"Go and find momma, please. Make her come to court. Get me out of here, please."

"Oh, I am," she said, then she hung up.

Chapter

38

I hurried up and went to sleep because my court date was in the morning. *Please lord, get me out of here.* I knew now we wouldn't make it to my birthday even though it was less than two months away.

When I got in court, low and behold granddaddy and momma were there. Granddaddy asked for me to be released. He didn't think they were going to take me to jail. My sister stood up and told them I could stay with her since I was about to turn eighteen.

So they released me into my sister's custody. She and her boyfriend had their own place. They released me, and momma and granddaddy were apologizing. I just looked at them. I went home and admittedly started packing my stuff.

"You need to come with me?" my sister asked.

"No, I'll be okay," I told her.

"Where're you going to go?" she asked.

"I'll think of something," I told her.

I called Shelia,

"Girl, where have you been?" she asked.

I started telling her all my troubles.

"Dang," she said, "you and Veronica can come here if you need to."

"Okay, thanks," I told her. "I'll call you in a few days."

I called Matt's momma and told her what happened.

"Baby, you need me to come to get you?" she asked.

"Not right now," I said. "I have to figure out what to do."

I still packed our stuff, not knowing where we were going to go.

The week was almost over, and when I got home, low and behold, Larry was sitting in the living room. He had gotten out of jail.

"Motherfucker!" I screamed.

I ran into granddaddy's room.

"You must have lost your goddamn mind. Why the fuck is Larry in here, and you got my motherfucking baby? Y'all must really want to die."

"He hasn't been near her," granddaddy said.

"Oh, hell fuck no!" I said. I grabbed Veronica, "I'm gone!."

"I'm not going to let him hurt her," he said, walking behind me. I went out the door.

"I'll come back to get the rest of my stuff," I said.

We got in the car and pulled off. I called Shelia and told her Veronica and I were coming over.

The next day I called my sister to meet me at granddaddy's house. I was going to get my stuff. I pulled up at granddaddy's house, and I was waiting in the car for my sister. She pulled up and got in the car with me.

"Girl, you're not gonna believe this," my sister said.

"What?" I asked.

"Granddaddy asked momma to let Larry stay with her since you got mad."

"That's stupid," I said. "What makes them think that's better?"

I don't know," she said.

We sat there in silence.

"Let's kill him," I said.

"I'm with you," she said. "If we get caught, I'll take the charge since you got that baby."

"Come on, let's get my stuff." We went into the back room, got all my stuff, and took it to Shelia's house.

When I got to Shelia's house, I was completely lost. Why in the hell would momma let him live with her? I went to work that day extremely sad. I sat in the break room crying.

A girl named Quinn came in there and asked why I was crying.

"I need somewhere to live," I told her.

My life was all messed up. I had started Chattanooga state and didn't know what I would do about my living situation.

"Go to the Westside," she told me in the back. "It's a social service office. Ask for a caseworker and tell them you're homeless."

"Ok, I'll tell them."

As soon as I got off from work, I did as she told me. When I went down there, the lady took my information and told me she would call me. She called within a week.

"Hey Tosha," she said, "I think I've got something for you."

"Oh, really, what?" I asked.

"I got the Eastlake project." I burst out crying. "What's wrong?" she said.

"I'm single with a young child, and I'm scared to stay out there by myself. Since I'm working, can't I get a scatter-site?"

"Let me see what I can find," she said.

It was about a month, and she called back.

"Tosha, now I know you're gonna like this," she said.

"Okay, what is it?"

"It's Cromwell," she said.

"Oh, thank you!" I said.

"Do you have fifty dollars?" she asked.

"Sure, do," I told her.

"Come bring it and sign your paperwork."

I was so happy I got off the phone and told everyone. I got down there with the money and filled out the paperwork.

"Since you just turned eighteen, we're gonna pull your juvenile record."

"Okay," I said, not thinking about the incident with granddaddy.

I went back to Shelia's house and started talking about furniture. I had the money, so I thought. Three days later, she called back.

"Tosha, we pulled your background, and you have a domestic assault on your record. I don't think I'll be able to approve you." I broke out crying. It was my only hope.

I called Matt, and I was crying uncontrollably. I told him what happened.

"Wait a minute, what did you say the lady's name was again?" he asked.

I repeated her name.

"I think I know her," he said.

I gave him the number, and he called her and set up a meeting.

"Now listen," he said, "when you go in here, don't you talk, let me talk to them."

"Okay," I told him.

We went in there, and Matt explained my troubles and said the only reason I acted out was because my momma had stolen my stuff and had a drug addiction. He assured them I was good

BREAKING THE CYCLE

and wouldn't give them any trouble. Lord Jesus! They agreed to give me a chance. She gave me my keys. We got outside and I gave him a big hug.

"Matt, thank you so much! You're going to be my friend for life."

"You're going to be crazy, Tosha," he said. "Come on, let's move your stuff."

Chapter

39

I was moving my stuff slowly because I had to get furniture. I was so happy. Even though momma and granddaddy welcomed Larry home, I was so happy I was calling them, anyway. I was telling my momma about all my plans.

"I need a little help," she said.

"What do you mean?" I asked.

"My car broke down, and I need to borrow some money to fix it," she said.

"Are you crazy!" I yelled. "I just got a place. I don't have anything. I'm not in a position to let someone borrow something. What's wrong with you?"

"I'm going to give it back," she said.

"You got all that money in the bank," she added.

I hung up. I forgot my bank statements still went to her house. I couldn't believe she was so selfish.

Granddaddy told me he had a friend on Main Street that sold furniture.

"Come, get me," he said, "I'll take you to Joe's. He will give you a deal."

The weekend came, and I went to get granddaddy to take him to Joe's. I picked out two-bedroom suites and a kitchen table. He told me it would be $2,200, and I was so happy. He also delivered.

I went to the bank to get the money out. I was walking out the door, looking at my receipt.

"Wait a minute; something isn't right," I said.

I went back to the bank.

"Hey, I'm missing some money," I told the teller, "$1,200."

She looked at the screen and went over the withdrawals,

"You took out $1,200," she said.

"No, I didn't," I said.

She went to get the branch manager because I was going off.

"Ms. Cook, they used your account number and withdrew the money," she said.

"Bullshit!" I said, "I didn't do it."

"Okay, I'll have to pull the camera," she said, "come back tomorrow and review it," I called my Aunt Liz.

"I think momma stole my money."

"Calm down," she said.

"The lady at the bank told me to come back at 1 PM the next day to look at the tape."

"Okay, I'll come with you," she said.

I called my sister to tell her what was going on.

"Well, momma said she needed to borrow some money to fix her car, and you were just sitting on it."

"So, it's mine."

"Well, she would've paid it back," she replied.

"Girl fuck," I hung up because I was about to curse her out.

They are flip-flopping people in the world. Now she's okay with momma stealing my money. The next day me and Aunt Liz headed to the bank. They took us to a room and played the tape. Of course, it was momma! And look who the driver was, my sister!

"Motherfucker!" I said.

I started screaming and yelling, and then I ran outside. My aunt came behind me.

"Calm down," she said.

"I'm going to kill their asses! How much can I take? How strong do y'all want me to be? I can't win with them, so I'm getting the hell away from them!"

She hugged me and took me back into the bank, where the bank manager was stunned.

"What you want to do?" she asked me.

"Press charges. I need my money back," I said. "The woman on the camera is my mother."

They contacted my momma, and she didn't deny it; she agreed to pay them back, so they put the money back in my account. My momma called me crying and apologizing, but I was just numb at this point.

I found a couch from some man selling stuff out of storage, but the couch was new. Matt moved it for me, and granddaddy gave me sheets and towels. Momma could wallpaper well, so she came and fixed up my bathroom for me.

Now we were finally stable where my stuff shouldn't be stolen anymore. You would think I would be happy, but I wasn't.

I was still crying every day. Something on the inside was missing; I was always sad. I had to figure my life out. I'll stay here to save some money then figure out where to go from here. I had been at Chattanooga State for two years now, and I started a new job working at Siskin Hospital.

Chapter

40

Siskin Hospital was pretty cool. I was working in the kitchen, and I met a girl named Leslie. She was about ten years older than me, but she was pretty nice. She had been there for a while, so she was showing me how to do stuff.

Granddaddy had Veronica that day. I called on break to see how she was doing. She sounded really sad.

"Veronica, what's wrong?" I asked.

"Jackie was talking about me."

"What do you mean?" I asked.

"She said it was about time my hair was combed, and they were laughing."

"I'll be over there," I told her.

I got right off work and went to granddaddy's house.

"Granddaddy, what was Jackie making Veronica cry for?" I asked.

"Hell, I don't know!" he said. "I told them to leave her alone."

"She wasn't going to be saying shit to my child like she did to me. You tell her she's going to see me."

Granddaddy didn't respond. Jackie's hatred ran so deep. She never bothered any of her other niece and nephews, except for my sister and me. She singled us out, and it was so obvious. They have fought and cursed us out since we were kids. She was not about to do my damn child like that.

About a week went by, and granddaddy called me down there to read some insurance papers for him. When I pulled up, guess who was there, Jackie? I got out of the car and went into the house. Jackie was sitting in the chair in the living room.

All I said was, "Jackie, what did you say to Veronica to make her cry?"

She jumped out of the chair and got right in my face.

"Bitch, don't say anything to me. That's why your momma is a junkie, and you ain't got shit," she said.

First, I stood there stunned because I didn't know what I said to get that reaction. Then I realized she was close enough to kiss me. So I pushed her.

"Get out of my face. What the hell is wrong with you? You're not going to be messing with my damn child, and I'm not playing!"

"Tosha, don't start that," granddaddy said.

"She's messing with me, and I'm not a kid anymore."

She was still cursing me. "Look at them, cars y'all got," she said.

I went out the door, and she followed me outside, still acting like a fool.

I called my sister and told her what was happening. Momma was over there with her.

"We're on our way," she said.

I sat in my car and waited on them. The next thing I heard was a striking noise. I looked up; they were coming around the corner on two wheels, literally. She pulled up in front of granddaddy's house, and Jackie was on the porch. My sister just jumped out of the car and didn't even put it in the park. Momma had to jump from the passenger's side to stop the car. My sister ran towards the house; Jackie ran into the house and locked the door. My sister started kicking and beating on the door.

Momma got out of the car, telling her to calm down.

"Tosha, you need to leave," granddaddy said.

"No, she started this shit, and I'm not playing about my baby. So she'd better not ever say shit else to her."

Jackie called the police. When the police came, she became bad. She came running out the door.

"These people came down to my daddy's house causing trouble."

"These people?" I said.

"These are her nieces," momma told the police officer.

"Jackie, stop arguing with their kids," momma said.

The police made us leave. She never said anything else to Veronica after that.

Chapter

41

I had been living in Cromwell for almost two years. The first two years, I paid fifty dollars a month. Now my rent would go up to four hundred dollars a month. I was at work one day talking to Leslie about it.

"Girl, they about to go up on my rent," I told her.

"Really?" she said. "To how much?"

"To four hundred dollars," I told her.

"Four hundred dollars!" she said. "You can buy a house for that."

"A house?" I replied. I didn't know anything about that.

"You can get just a little small one like mine," she said.

"Really? I'm only nineteen years old."

"That doesn't matter," she told me. "I'll give you the guy's name and the number that helped me,"

"Well, okay," I told her.

I called the man named Chris.

"Hey, Leslie gave me your number."

"Oh, okay, I'll be glad to help you," he told me.

He took me looking for houses, but I wasn't seeing anything I liked at first. Leslie told me not to go over forty-thousand dollars so my mortgage would stay under five hundred dollars. I was a little scared, but either way, I would have to pay rent. I had been saving money as well.

"Well, your credit is pretty good," he told me, "so I'll call a lender for you to help you get a loan."

"What's a lender?" I asked.

"Someone to get you financed."

All the information they were giving me was overwhelming. Plus, I had no idea what I was doing. I called Leslie on everything.

"Girl, I'm scared," I told her.

"You will be alright," she told me. "Hell! Either way, you got to pay rent,"

"Yes, that's right."

"Just stick with Chris; he will show you the right way. He's good. Don't worry. He helped me, too," she said.

"Okay," I said.

I felt better but still had a little anxiety. The next week Chris called me.

"Tosha, I found the perfect house."

"You did?" I said.

"Yes, and it's newly remodeled. It's been on the market for a while, and the owner is ready to get rid of it. He wants fifty-thousand," he told me.

"I didn't want to go over forty-thousand," I told him.

"I know," he said, "I'm sure we can talk him down."

"Okay, if you think so."

We met with the owner, and Chris told him I was a single parent and didn't have much money. He told him that I was just getting started. The owner told him he would sell it to me for forty-two thousand dollars. We agreed.

It was a small cute house, with a garage in the back. It had a small porch. As you walked in, there was a living room, dining room, and the freshly painted kitchen. Outside the kitchen was a small back porch that was screened in and had a door attached to it where you could walk down the steps to the backyard. It had a small driveway. The full bathroom and two bedrooms were of nice size. It was perfect for my daughter and me. The lender approved my loan, and at nineteen years old, I purchased my first house.

Epilogue

After I purchased my first house, I got a good job at Shaw Insurance. My credit score was good enough that I was able to buy a brand new 2001 Nissan Xterra at twenty-one years of age.

Granddaddy called one day; he wanted to talk. I went down there, and he told me he wouldn't be here much longer. I cried.

"I'm getting old," he said, "I'm ready to go."

"Granddaddy, what I'm going to do?" I asked.

"You will be okay,' he said.

He told me to get life insurance on all of us (meaning my mother, myself, and my daughter) because he had cashed all our policies in. So I went and got us all insurance. Then, he told me he would adopt my daughter so, when he died, she could draw social security check off him. That way, he would still be helping me take care of her since he made her his responsibility because her father still never helped.

He woke momma up and told her to come to put the house he bought her in her name. He told her if something happened to him, her sisters would fight her for that house. He told us the rest of the family was not going to help us, so we would have to stick together.

Right before my twenty-third birthday, my momma got locked up and got a ten-year sentence, and was shipped off to prison.

At twenty-three, I purchased another home and rented the first house. The renting business was short-lived. After a couple of years, my momma got out of prison because I filed appeals until she got released.

Granddaddy went to the hospital on New Year's eve of 2003. He passed away in February 2004. The week before he passed away, I went to see him in the hospital. The whole time he was hospitalized, he hadn't talked. This day as I was coming down the hallway, I could see him looking out the window. It was like he was looking for someone.

I went in; he smiled and said, "I love you."

I cried and ran to him.

He said, "You know you have to pay the taxes on your momma house. Don't let her lose that house."

"I won't, granddaddy," I promised.

He laid back and never spoke another word. I kept my promise.

At age thirty-two, I purchased my third and final home. I'm currently renovating it to make it my forever dream home. I'm designing it myself.

To my readers, this whole journey was personal for me. I wrote this book to help anyone that has been abused and mistreated and thought you couldn't tell anyone.

No matter how bad your situation is, speak your peace, do not live in fear. I cried many nights, but the joy did come in the morning. You can overcome anything because GOD IS. He is a Healer. He is a Deliverer, and He can restore your soul like He did mine.

Do not let anyone discourage you from anything you think is worth your time. Your goals and dreams are yours, and no one can take them away from you. Aim high, be encouraged, and be blessed.

Made in United States
Orlando, FL
09 March 2022

15610684R00135